DID MAN GET HERE BY EVOLUTION OR BY CREATION?

IN almost all countries throughout the world the doctrine of evolution is taught. School textbooks on biology and history present evolution as established fact. Evolutionary teaching saturates science, philosophy, history and even religion today. Whenever the subject of the origin of life and man is discussed, it is almost always presented in evolutionary terms. But what do you personally know of the evidence for or against the belief in evolution? Does it really harmonize with the facts of science? We invite your careful examination of this matter, as it has a direct bearing on your life and your future.

—THE PUBLISHERS

CONTENTS

CHAPTER 1

Is Evolution an Established Fact?

ARE you a descendant of an apelike beast that lived millions of years ago?

Sooner or later this question confronts almost everyone, especially students in the school systems of this world. The instructors and textbooks of these students teach that man did descend from the beasts by the process of evolution.

On the other hand, the Bible teaches that God created man, and all kinds of life, directly and not by a process of evolution. Has there been so much evidence for evolution that this Bible teaching is obsolete? Is evolution a fact? Does it hold the key to the future of mankind? And, too, does it really make any difference whether man evolved from the animals or not? Does it affect our lives?

ORGANIC EVOLUTION

Evolution, in the sense that it is applied to plants, animals and man is said to be the transforming of one kind of life into another kind. A writer in the Houston *Post* of August 23, 1964, defined it this way: "Evolution, in very simple terms, means that life progressed from one-celled organisms to its highest state, the human being, by means of a series of biological changes taking place over millions of years."[1] Another source, *The River of Life,* stated: "When living things came out of the sea to live on land, fins turned into legs, gills into lungs, scales into fur."[2] And the 1966 *World Book Encyclopedia* said:

> "The theory of organic evolution involves these three main ideas: (1) Living things change from generation to generation, producing descendants with new characteristics. (2) This process has been going on so long that it has produced all the groups and kinds of things now living, as well as others that lived long ago and have died out, or become extinct. (3) These different living things are related to each other."[3]

Mere change within a basic type of living thing is not to be regarded as evolution. That is simply variety, as we can observe among all plants, animals and man. For instance, there are various sizes, shapes and colors of cats, but such is only variety and in itself does not constitute organic evolution.

Regarding the period of time thought to be involved in the process, Professor T. Dobzhansky writes in his book *Genetics and the Origin of Species* that it "is surmised to be of the order of two billion [2,000,000,000] years . . . from causes which now continue to be in operation, and which therefore can be studied experimentally."[4]

Although some evolutionists believe that a Creator began the process, most today teach that life arose from inanimate matter without any divine assistance. Their feeling was expressed at the Chicago Darwinian centennial in 1959 by prominent evolutionist Sir Julian Huxley, who said that "evolution had no room for the supernatural. The earth and its inhabitants were not created, they evolved."[5]

ACCEPTED AS FACT

At the same conference Huxley told the 2,500 assembled delegates: "We all accept the fact of evolution. . . . The evolution of life is no longer a theory. It is a fact. It is the basis of all our thinking."[6] The 1963 book *Biology for You* confirms this by saying: "All reputable biologists have agreed that the evolution of life on the earth is an established fact."[7]

The majority of educators also accept evolution. One university president from the United States said:

"It takes an overwhelming prejudice to refuse to accept the facts, and anyone who is exposed to the evidence supporting evolution must recognize it as an historical fact."[8]

Even many religious leaders hold this view. The Milwaukee *Journal* of March 5, 1966, reported that the "pastor of St. James Catholic church . . . made a firm statement accepting evolution. 'There is no doubt about the fact of evolution,' " he said. The account related that the priest "underlined the word 'fact.' "[9]

The general acceptance of evolution can be noted in the account of an astronaut who performed experiments outside his orbiting spacecraft. An editorial in the New York *Times* of November 14, 1966, commented: "All the reflexes and instincts incorporated in his mind and body as the result of millions of years of organic evolution here on earth were severely tested by exposure to the weirdly different milieu of space."[10]

Thus today the vast majority of those who influence the thinking of people, in both noncommunist and Communist lands alike, accept evolution as a fact. And a fact, as *Webster's Third New International Dictionary* tells us, is "an actual happening in time or space," a "verified statement."[11]

IS IT A FACT?

However, when analyzing more deeply the comments of those who consider evolution an established fact, a truly amazing situation develops. It is one that the average person is probably not aware of, one that has few parallels in any other field of science.

Over a hundred years ago, in 1859, evolutionist Charles Darwin stated in chapter six of his book *The Origin of Species:* "Long before the reader has arrived at this part of my work, a crowd of difficulties will have occurred to him. Some of them are so serious that to this day I can hardly reflect on them without being in some degree staggered."[12] How much of a "fact" was evolution in Darwin's day if he was "staggered" by its difficulties?

Has more than a century of intensive investigation since Darwin's time clearly verified evolution as a "fact"? *Science Year* of 1966 reported: "Archaeology, despite its triumphs, remains almost at the beginning of the immense task of reconstructing mankind's history."[13] A "beginning" certainly cannot be considered the same as an established "fact."

This paradox is heightened by the renowned evolutionist Professor Dobzhansky in his book *The Biological Basis of Human Freedom.* He first declares: "Evolution as a historical fact was proved beyond reasonable doubt not later than in the closing decades of the nineteenth century." But then, just two pages later, he says: "There is no doubt that both the historical and the causal aspects of the evolutionary process are far from completely known. . . . The causes which have brought about the development of the human species can be only dimly discerned."[14]

On one hand evolution is declared to be a fact, but on the other it is acknowledged that the process is "far from completely known," the causes "only dimly discerned," the difficulties "staggering."

These are not isolated cases. The *Encyclopædia Britannica* stated: "We are not in the least doubt as to the fact of evolution. . . . The evidence by now is overwhelming." But a few pages later it called that evidence "very imperfect and often interrupted by gaps." It added: "Of the vital processes which brought about these changes we are as yet ignorant."[15]

Famous evolutionist Sir Gavin de Beer, in his recent biography *Charles Darwin,* writes: "He [Darwin] predicted that the evidence would one day be forthcoming, and that day has arrived, for the series of fossils just mentioned provides the crucial evidence that man did evolve."[16] Yet, in 1964, in the book *The Fossil Evidence for Human Evolution,* written by another prominent evolutionist, W. Le Gros Clark, we read:

"The chances of finding the fossil remains of *actual* ancestors, or even representatives of the local geographical group which provided the actual ancestors, are so fantastically remote as not to be worth consideration."

"The interpretation of the paleontological evidence of hominid evolution which has been offered in the preceding chapters is a provisional interpretation. Because of the incompleteness of the evidence, it could hardly be otherwise."[17]

When *Science* magazine, in 1965, reviewed the book *The Basis of Human Evolution,* it stated: "The reader . . . may be dumbfounded that so much work has settled so few questions."[18] And in the 1966 *World Book Encyclopedia* we read: "No one should make the mistake of saying that evolution is fully understood."[19] Also, *Science News Letter* said in 1965: "The fight is among scientists over just how man did evolve, when he did so and what he looked like."[20]

Can any process be called a fact, "an actual happening," a "verified statement," when the knowledge of *how, when, where, what* and *why* is missing? If someone stated that it was a fact that a skyscraper evolved by itself from a brick on an empty lot, but that how, when, where and why it did so, and what it looked like in the process, were not known, would you consider the transformation a fact or just an assertion?

That the teaching of evolution cannot be called a scientific fact is shown in this statement by evolutionist Clark: "What was the ultimate origin of man? . . . Unfortunately, any answers which can at present be given to these questions are based on indirect evidence and thus are largely conjectural."[21]

This is also acknowledged by a former president of the American Association for the Advancement of Science. Writing in *Science* magazine in support of evolution, he said:

> "Come, now, if you will, on a *speculative* excursion into prehistory. *Assume* the era in which the species sapiens emerged from the genus Homo . . . hasten across the millenniums for which present information depends for the most part on *conjecture* and *interpretation* to the era of the first inscribed records, from which some facts may be gleaned."[22] [Italics ours]

The age of inscribed records began several thousand years ago. The evolutionary process that is thought to have preceded it is admittedly based on conjecture, interpretation, speculation and pyramiding hypotheses. And of Darwin's famous book, *The Origin of Species*, British scientist L. M. Davies once said:

> "It has been estimated that no fewer than 800 phrases in the subjunctive mood (such as 'Let us assume,' or 'We may well suppose,' etc.) are to be found between the covers of Darwin's *Origin of Species* alone."[23]

The sincere inquirer cannot help but be struck by this situation. Evolutionists dogmatically assert that evolution is a fact, yet admit that all the important conclusions are conjectural!

Indeed, one scientist, Dr. T. N. Tahmisian, a physiologist for the Atomic Energy Commission, said: "Scientists who go about teaching that evolution is a fact of life are great con men, and the story they are telling may be the greatest hoax ever. In explaining evolution we do not have one iota of fact." He called it "a tangled mishmash of guessing games and figure juggling."[24] Another scientist, head of a college science department, J. W. Klotz, stated in 1965 that "acceptance of evolution is still based on a great deal of faith."[25]

To understand better how this conflicting situation came about, it is helpful to look at the background of the evolution theory. Let us consider the following questions: When did the modern ideas of evolution begin? How have they developed? What is the current status of the theory? Why is there so much confusion and contradiction among evolutionists themselves? And if we apply the truly scientific method of observing all the facts first and then drawing conclusions, what do they show?

CHAPTER 2

Development of Evolutionary Theory

ALTHOUGH some ancient philosophers entertained what might be called evolutionary ideas, none of these gained any wide acceptance. Also, in the Middle Ages zoological writings contained recipes reputed to produce such things as flies, bees and even mice from nonliving matter. But it was not until the last two centuries that the theory of organic evolution gained any real prominence.

Among the first earlier theories to gain acceptance were those of the English naturalist Erasmus Darwin [grandfather of Charles Darwin], and French scientist Comte de Buffon, in the eighteenth century. They maintained that when a plant or an animal acquired a new characteristic from its environment, it could pass this on to its offspring, resulting in changes that accounted for evolution. For example, they contended that the thick armor-like skin in some animals developed because they received repeated blows. This characteristic, they claimed, was then passed on to their offspring, which were born with thicker skin.

In the early nineteenth century French scientist Jean de Lamarck published a book agreeing with the theory of acquired characteristics, but said it was the needs of organisms that gave the driving force to evolution. According to his theory, giraffes got long necks because they ran out of vegetation and had to stretch their necks to obtain leaves higher up on trees. In this way, each generation passed on to its offspring a slightly longer neck.

How widespread was the belief in acquired characteristics in those days? In his book *Charles Darwin* evolutionist De Beer answers: "Nobody would have thought of doubting it till the close of the nineteenth century . . . The number of men before the nineteenth century who rejected the inheritance of acquired characters could be counted on the fingers of one hand."[26]

However, at the close of the nineteenth century German scientist August Weismann tried to establish a breed of tailless mice by simply cutting off their tails before allowing them to mate. A 1966 textbook, *Review Text in Biology,* tells of the results:

> "He repeated this procedure for 20 successive generations. The last generation proved to have tails as long as those of their ancestors. This was the first experimental proof that acquired characteristics, such as artificial taillessness, are not inherited. . . .
>
> "Acquired characteristics are not inherited because environmental factors (which do not affect the genes in the sex cells) cannot influence the next generation."[27]

Nobel Prize-winning geneticist H. J. Muller also said:

> "Despite the strong influence of the environment in modifying the body as a whole, and even the protoplasm of its cells, the genes within the germ-cells of that body retain their original structure without specific alterations caused by the

modification of the body, so that when the modified-individual reproduces it transmits to its offspring genes unaffected by its own 'acquired characters.'"[28]

Although true scientific facts exploded completely the evolutionary theory of acquired characteristics, it did not die out completely. The 1960

Traits acquired during lifetime, such as artificially enlarged lips, not passed on to offspring

book *The Mechanism of Evolution,* by W. H. Dowdeswell, relates: "The last of the Lamarckist revivals took place in Russia in 1948 under the leadership of Lysenko, but the claims of his school are now discredited and appear to have been activated largely by ideological rather than scientific motives."[29] Later, *Time* magazine of February 12, 1965, reported that Lysenko was removed from his position and his theories rejected even by the Communists, noting that heredity "is controlled by genes in the reproductive cells and remains unchanged throughout an individual's life."[30]

The greatest impetus for evolution came with the writings of Charles Darwin, particularly in 1859 with the publishing of his book *The Origin of Species.* Darwin's theory was that members of different species competed with one another for life, and that in such struggle any advantageous variation would enable its possessor to gain the upper hand. The fittest, therefore, would survive, the others would perish. The survivors would pass on the beneficial variations to their offspring, accounting eventually for the evolution of new forms of life. Darwin called this process "natural selection."

We might illustrate Darwin's belief with the giraffe. For an unknown reason some giraffes were born with slightly longer necks than others. The ones with longer necks won the competition for food, therefore survived ("natural selection") and passed on a slightly longer neck to their offspring. This was repeated for many generations, thus supposedly accounting for long-necked giraffes.

As time passed, however, objections to Darwin's position appeared. This is called to our attention in the 1964 textbook *Biology for Today,* by Clark and Mould:

> "Scientists have raised a number of objections against complete acceptance of Darwin's theory. . . . 1. The theory does not account for all the known facts of heredity. For example, the theory does not clearly explain why some variations are inherited and others are not. Many variations are so trivial that they could not possibly aid an organism in its struggle for existence. 2. The theory does not explain how the gradual accumulation of trivial variations could result in the appearance of some of the more complex structures found in higher organisms."[31]

In the book *The Story of Life* evolutionist H. Mellersh notes:

> "On the Darwinian theory, the questioner may point out, any variation has to be of *immediate* value to its possessor if it is going to give him a better chance of survival than his fellows. Of what 'survival value' is the first dim beginnings of

an eye, or forelimbs starting to flap about feebly and nakedly in anticipation of a wing? ... Natural Selection is so *mindless*. It is so purposeless."[32]

Hence, Darwin's theory, as he presented it, was proved faulty and many aspects of it were rejected. The next major step in evolution came in 1901. Dutch botanist Hugo De Vries had been experimenting with plants known as evening primroses. He noticed that occasionally some appeared with unusual structures and that their offspring inherited these same traits. He called these *mutants*. De Vries believed that favorable large mutations accounted for evolution. For example, giraffes with unusually long necks, mutants, appeared and survived better than did short-necked giraffes. These mutants produced offspring with long necks, supposedly accounting for this bit of evolution.

This new theory did not remain unchallenged for long. Difficulties soon became apparent. Concerning the sudden large changes that De Vries claimed were responsible for evolution De Beer comments:

"Many of them had lethal results and killed the organisms that carried them, ... far from conferring improvement in adaptation, the mutations seemed to be pathological, and provided no explanation of how adaptations arose and became perfected. The result ... was that during the first twenty years of the twentieth century, evolutionary studies and theories were in a state of chaos and confusion."[33]

Summarizing these principal theories of evolution noted so far, Hall and Lesser's 1966 *Review Text in Biology* states:

"Since Lamarck's theory [acquired characteristics] has been proved false, it is only of historical interest. Darwin's theory [natural selection] does not satisfactorily explain the origin and inheritance of variations. ... De Vries' theory [large mutations] has been shown to be weak because no single mutation or set of mutations has ever been so large and numerous that it has been known to start a new species in one generation of offspring."[34]

Has this chaos of theories been cleared up in our day? What is the current theory accepted by most evolutionists? Has it proved more plausible? Is it more scientific?

MODERN THEORY

In recent years a new theory has been advanced, one that many evolutionists accept. This modern theory includes some of the views of Darwin and De Vries. Professor C. P. Martin of McGill University defines it by observing in *American Scientist:* "An overwhelming majority of [biologists] believe that evolution proceeds by mutations and natural selection."[35]

The modern theory says that a beneficial small mutation appeared in a particular organism. That mutation made its possessor better suited to survive than were its competitors. The beneficial small mutation was passed along by heredity through many generations. Over a period of millions of years other beneficial mutations continued to appear in the same line, causing the organism to change into a different one. Summing up the modern theory, the Oklahoma City *Times* of August 10, 1966, said: "Accidental alterations in the mechanism of his heredity slowly—by trial and error—made man better adapted to his environment than are his rivals. That's the accepted scientific view today, and scientists call this long, frequently bungling process 'evolution.' "[36] Also, since the modern theory includes part of Darwin's belief in "natural selection," it is often referred to as "neo-Darwinism."

To illustrate the modern theory we might again refer to the giraffe. In past ages the ancestors of modern giraffes were said to have short necks. As they struggled for existence the giraffes competed for leaves on trees. Some giraffes happened to be mutants that had slightly longer necks. These survived in greater numbers, as they could eat leaves higher up on trees. The short-necked giraffes died out, and those with the longer necks were left to produce offspring. These supposedly continued the process until the giraffe's neck reached its present length.

Many evolutionists claim that finally a theory has been devised that adequately explains things. As the world-famous biologist and evolutionist Jean Rostand stated: "For them, then, the problem of evolution has been thoroughly, completely, and definitely, re-

French scientists ask: "Can there live side by side two cousins, each of them fitter than the other, one because its neck is longer, the other because its neck is shorter?"

solved. With mutation and natural selection, the perfect explanation is at our disposal."[37]

At this point, though, we are confronted with the same amazing dilemma noted earlier, because the modern theory has not at all settled the matter. The controversy still rages! Information such as the following in *Science Digest* of January 1961 shows this. In an article entitled "Should We Burn Darwin?" the writer states:

"Perhaps the most significant single fact in last year's development of French scientific thought is that the above orthodox explanation of evolution has been badly shaken. Often criticized in the past, it has now come under such heavy fire that the way seems to be open, in France at least, to a new theory of the origin of species. . . .

"These are a few of the embarrassing questions asked today by the French rebels: If the giraffe with its eight-foot neck is the product of natural selection and an example of the survival of the fittest, what about the sheep with its neck no longer than a few inches? Aren't giraffes and sheep very close cousins, almost brethren in the animal kingdom . . . ? But then can there live side by side two cousins, each of them fitter than

| Shropshire Ram | Dorset Horn Ram |

If sheep evolved horns because they aided survival, why are there many hornless varieties of sheep that survive just as well without them?

the other, one because its neck is longer, the other because its neck is shorter?

"And talking of sheep, what about their horns? According to the classical school they started growing freakishly, and then, as they proved an asset in the sheep's struggle for life, nature went on selecting the horned animals and eliminating the hornless ones. But did it really? There are at least as many hornless sheep as those with horns. Which of them are fitter? ...

"Out of 120,000 fertilized eggs of the green frog only two individuals survive. Are we to conclude that these two frogs out of 120,000 were selected by nature because they were the fittest ones; or rather ... that natural selection is nothing but blind mortality which selects nothing at all?"[38]

Another example of the attack being leveled against the modern theory is that made by the prominent evolutionist Jean Rostand. In his 1961 publication *The Orion Book of Evolution* Rostand says:

"Is it really certain, then, as the neo-Darwinists maintain, that the problem of evolution is ... a settled matter ... ? I, personally, do not think so, and, along with a good many others, I must insist on raising some banal objections to the doctrine of neo-Darwinism ...

"The mutations which we know and which are considered responsible for the creation of the living world are, in general, either organic deprivations, deficiencies (loss of pigment, loss of an appendage), or the doubling of the pre-existing organs. In any case, they never produce anything really new or original in the organic scheme, nothing which one might consider the basis for a new organ or the priming for a new function. ...

"No, decidedly, I cannot make myself think that these 'slips' of heredity have been able, even with the cooperation of natural selection, even with the advantage of the immense periods of time in which evolution works on life, to build the entire world, with its structural prodigality and refinements, its astounding 'adaptations,' ... I cannot persuade myself to think that the eye, the ear, the human brain have been formed in this way; . . . I discern nothing that gives me the right to conceive the profound structural alterations, the fantastic metamorphoses that we have to imagine in evolutionary history when we think of the transition from invertebrates to vertebrates, from fish to batrachians, from batrachians to reptiles, from reptiles to mammals."[39]

After rejecting or questioning all the major theories, Rostand asks: "Will the future surprise us with a great new idea about the mechanism of evolution? We should certainly not exclude this hope, but it is difficult to restrain a certain scepticism." But then he concludes: "Despite this rather disillusioned conclusion, it is of paramount importance that no excuse be found to cast doubt upon the fact of evolution itself."[40]

But the honest investigator will do just that! After several centuries of conflicting theories, arguments and assertions, it must be obvious to the unprejudiced inquirer that evolution is not a fact at all, but is pure theory, and that it must be challenged to arrive at the truth.

HOW SCIENTIFIC?

There is another aspect of the matter that needs to be considered. It was noted in a December 3, 1966, *Saturday Evening Post* article supporting evolution:

"Among [evolutionists] leading the current research . . . feelings often run high when it comes to interpreting evidence. Criticism is sometimes regarded, and perhaps intended, as a deep personal insult.

"Not long ago a professor wrote an article questioning a former teacher, in the mildest possible terms, about the authenticity of a certain find—and ended a friendship of 30 years. On another occasion an eminent anthropologist arose to speak at a meeting given in his honor, and began reminiscing about the early days of his career when his ideas concerning human evolution had been ignored. But he managed to complete only a few sentences of his talk. Then, overcome by the recollection of years of frustration, he lowered his head and burst into tears. Investigators have stalked out of meetings, indulged in personal vituperation, argued over priorities, accused colleagues of stealing their ideas.

"Such behavior . . . has been strikingly high among prehistorians. The reason for this occupational ailment is obscure, but it may have something to do with the shortage of solid evidence. . . . sometimes the less excavators have to go on, the more ardently they stick to their guns."[41]

In trying to account for such strikingly peculiar, even juvenile, behavior on the part of evolutionary scientists, the article adds: " 'I can't account for it,' says an anthropologist who has been in the thick of a number of fights, 'but there is something about exploring the past that affects you. It seems that every time a man finds a human bone he goes crazy on the spot.' "

All of this is positive evidence that the truly scientific method has not, and is not, being applied to the theories on evolution. The facts have not forced conclusions, but the preconceived conclusions of evolutionists have forced the facts.

The method correctly called scientific is that which analyzes all the facts available first, and then draws conclusions. This the unprejudiced investigator can do, for many proved scientific facts are at his disposal. These will allow each one to judge for himself on the basis of solid evidence alone and to draw honest conclusions, conclusions that are not based on ego, petty differences, a search for glory and advancement, or on preconceived notions. From such facts what conclusion can be drawn regarding the origin of life?

CHAPTER 3

Does Life Come from Nonliving Matter?

EVOLUTION asserts that the first speck of life on earth arose by itself from inanimate matter. All matter on earth is composed of basic chemical elements. An element is a substance made up entirely of atoms of one single kind, and cannot be simplified or decomposed by ordinary chemical means.

Is there any trend toward evolution among the elements on earth? No, for atoms are generally found to be either stable or, in the case of some, in a decaying trend until they turn into an element that is stable.

This fact harmonizes with the scientific principle called "entropy." This essentially means that there is a tendency from the highly organized *downward* toward the less organized. Never is there an increase of order without an outside force. To illustrate: will the elements of earth, left to themselves, ever produce an automobile, or even a simple gear? To the contrary, the elements remain as they are. When they are fashioned into a machine by man, even the machine, when left to itself, begins to decay.

For another illustration take a large barrel and put into it bits of steel, glass, rubber and other materials. Turn the barrel thousands of times and open it. Would you ever find that the materials by themselves had produced a complete automobile? All you would *ever* find is a mixture of the materials, no matter how often you tried the experiment. From this fact we can conclude a fundamental truth.

Inanimate matter on earth simply does not search out a way to improve itself, but tends toward the state of neutralization or stability. Nor will an appeal to immense periods of time help. Time produces decay, disintegration. It results in corroding metals, eroding cliffs. Time is destructive, not constructive. It is the enemy of evolution.

The principle of inertia also confirms this. Inertia is the tendency of all objects to stay still if still, or if moving, to go on moving in the same direction unless acted on by some outside force. A ball will not pick itself off the ground and throw itself to the catcher. A wagon will not move by itself unless acted upon by a superior force. Inanimate matter, devoid of motion, energy and life to begin with, would have stayed inanimate forever unless acted upon by a superior outside force that could give it direction and organization.

In the publication *Discovery* of May 1962 a review of R. Schubert-Soldern's book *Mechanism and Vitalism* stated:

> " 'All molecules result from an electro-chemical tendency to neutralisation. They are therefore expressions of tendencies toward stability.' Unhappily for materialists, however, life is characteristically *un*stable, and 'it is incredible that a complex of substances, all tending towards a state of stability, would produce the permanent chemical instability which is characteristic of animate matter.' Thus it is inconceivable that an organic compound should ever be formed in the absence of life: 'No condition of inorganic matter is even thinkable in which carbon, oxygen and

Wagon will not move by itself unless acted upon by outside force

Machine left to itself decays, as inanimate matter tends downward, not upward

Time produces disintegration, eroding cliffs. It is destructive, not constructive

Ball will not pick itself up off the ground

hydrogen could combine to form a sugar rather than water and carbon dioxide.'"[42]

So the facts reveal no upward evolving of the elements on earth, either into more complex elements or into organic compounds. But for evolution to have taken place, the inanimate elements would have had to evolve, and not just into another element or organic compound either, but into something far, far more complicated. They would have had to evolve into a living cell.

THE LIVING CELL

The gap between the inanimate elements of earth and a living cell is gigantic. In the finest laboratories the simple cell cannot be created from inanimate matter. Even if it could, that would prove that the elements need a directing force to produce a living substance.

We should not think of a single cell as being so simple that there would be no difficulty in its arising by itself from inanimate matter. *Look* magazine declared in its January 16, 1962, issue: "The cell is as complicated as New York City."[43]

The more carefully a single cell is studied, the more complex it is found to be. German biologist Von Bertalanffy said, as noted by evolutionist L. Eiseley in his book *The Immense Journey:* "To grasp in detail the physico-chemical organization of the simplest cell is far beyond our capacity."[44] Sir James Gray, professor of zoology from Cambridge University, concurs, in *Science Today:*

> "A bacterium is far more complex than any inanimate system known to man. There is not a laboratory in the world which can compete with the biochemical activity of the smallest living organism."[45]

In the book *The Ideas of Biology* evolutionist J. T. Bonner observes:

"The cell is really such an astoundingly clever unit that when we think of it from the point of view of evolution it seems easier to imagine a single cell evolving into complex animals and plants than it does to imagine a group of chemical substances evolving into a cell. It is very likely that the first step was more difficult ... The study of early evolution really amounts to educated guesswork."[46]

The science section of the New York *Times* of November 13, 1966, said of a plant cell:

"The largest single manufacturing process in the world takes place in one of the smallest units of life—cells of green plants.

"The manufacturing process is ... photosynthesis. Each year this process accounts for the transformation of 100 billion tons of the inorganic element carbon into organic forms that support life.

"By contrast, all the big blast furnaces of the world make only a half-billion tons of steel in the same time."[47]

The complexity and productivity of these cells are not facts that support the conclusions of evolution. Since the complexity and productivity of a blast furnace are facts from which we conclude that it was designed by an intelligent mind, should not the same conclusion be drawn from the facts about a cell?

The neuron, or nerve cell, demonstrates how complicated a cell is. There are said to be at least 10,000,000,000 such cells in the brain of one person. At one time each neuron was thought to be like a simple relay or telephone switchboard. But further research has revealed that a neuron is far more complicated than a complex electronic computer. If scientists invented a self-programming computer of infinite complexity only one-thousandth of an inch long, would this not be a

A computer did not evolve by itself from inanimate matter. Yet, a living cell is far more complicated than the most complex computer

monumental achievement? Would anyone listen very long to a claim that it came into existence by itself, that it evolved from inanimate matter without the direction of an intelligent mind?

When a cell is compared with a book, the facts reveal that the book is much less complicated and far, far easier to make. Yet, a book has to have an intelligent author and printer. It does not come into being by itself. Webster's unabridged dictionary took 757 editor-years to produce, not including the time of typists, photocopiers, clerical assistants, and the time of over two hundred consultants, to say nothing of the many men required to print and assemble it in the factory.[48] No one would ever contend that it all happened due to a chance coordination of ink molecules. It had to have intelligent direction. Since a cell is more complex, should not the same conclusion be drawn from the facts about it? It was with good reason that Princeton University biology professor Edwin Conklin once said: "The probability of life originating from accident is comparable to the probability of the unabridged dictionary resulting from an explosion in a printing shop."[49]

In this regard note what the well-known evolutionist and anthropologist Loren Eiseley says in his book *The Immense Journey:*

"Intensified effort revealed that even the supposedly simple amoeba was a complex, self-operating chemical factory. The notion that he was a simple blob, the discovery of whose chemical composition would enable us instantly to set the life process in operation, turned out to be, at best, a monstrous caricature of the truth.

"With the failure of these many efforts science was left in the somewhat embarrassing position of having to postulate theories of living origins which it could not demonstrate. After having chided the theologian for his reliance on myth and miracle, science found itself in the unenviable position of having to create a mythology of its own: namely, the assumption that what, after long effort, could not be proved to take place today had, in truth, taken place in the primeval past."[50]

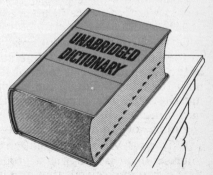

A book does not result from a chance coordination of ink molecules or an accident in a printing factory, yet it is simple compared to a single living cell

Such theorizing runs directly counter to the evidence showing that the inanimate elements of the earth do not of themselves evolve upward into living organisms. Dr. Eiseley acknowledged this:

> "One does occasionally observe, however, a tendency for the beginning zoological textbook to take the unwary reader by a hop, skip, and jump from the little steaming pond or the beneficent chemical crucible of the sea, into the lower world of life with such sureness and rapidity that it is easy to assume that there is no mystery about this matter at all, or, if there is, that it is a very little one.

> "This attitude has indeed been sharply criticized by the distinguished British biologist Woodger, who remarked some years ago: 'Unstable organic compounds and chlorophyll corpuscles do not persist or come into existence in nature on their own account at the present day, and consequently it is necessary to postulate that conditions were once such that this did happen although and in spite of the fact that our knowledge of nature does not give us any warrant for making such a supposition . . . It is simple dogmatism—asserting that what you want to believe did in fact happen.' "[51]

Of the living cell, evolutionist Rutherford Platt in the book *The River of Life* states: "So perfect is the original one-cell form of life, and so potent both for body building, for activating nerves and muscles, and for procreation, that the cell has never altered its basic size or nature from the beginning of life even to this day."[52]

Why not? Why has evolution not continued to improve upon it if it was a product of evolution? Was it just an accident that this infinitely complex mechanism was perfect to begin with? Since when has any man-made piece of machinery come into existence without years of improvement and perfecting? No man has been able to introduce a perfect machine that never needed improvement, not even the world's greatest genius. Yet a cell is just such a mechanism. How scientific is it for evolution to conclude, without facts, that inanimate, unintelligent elements did what no human genius can do?

FROM WHERE DOES LIFE COME?

The theory of the evolution of a living cell from nonliving matter is really just a refined version of the older theory of spontaneous generation, which, step by step, was discredited by true scientific facts. *Review Text in Biology* tells about it:

> "Francesco Redi, an Italian physician, was the first (about 1688) to carry out controlled experiments that disproved the belief that maggots arose from decaying fish, snakes, and meat. . . . Redi proved that maggots and flies arise from living parents, not from dead matter.
>
> "Lazzaro Spallanzani, an Italian priest (about 1780), sealed numerous vegetable juices in glass flasks and then boiled them. After allowing these materials to cool and stand for a number of days, Spallanzani could not observe any organisms. Even microscopic examination did not reveal them. Spallanzani concluded that nothing developed in the juices because boiling killed any

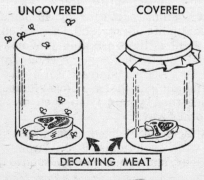

UNCOVERED   COVERED

DECAYING MEAT

Maggots in meat came from eggs deposited by flies. When jar cover kept flies out, no maggots appeared

living organisms that might have been present. Consequently, there were no living organisms to give rise to new ones.

"Louis Pasteur, a French scientist (about 1860), conclusively demonstrated that microorganisms, which are present everywhere, get into organic matter, which serves as their food. After feeding and growing, the microorganisms reproduce and thereby give rise to many others like themselves. If flasks containing food are sealed and sterilized, ... even after many months, no microorganisms appear."[53]

The origin of any life, however "simple," is really based on the scientific principle of biogenesis. Of this principle *The Encyclopedia Americana* says:

"From the Greek words *bios*, life, and *genesis*, birth, source, creation, is the biological term for the doctrine that living organisms are produced only by other living organisms, ... biologists are now not only in virtually unanimous agreement that all life derives from preceding life, but that the parent organism and its offspring are of the same *kind*."[54]

This exactly fits the scientific facts, which demonstrate that inanimate matter by itself is never seen building up life of any kind. Only when life is already present is there possibility of new life. As the 1963 book *Biology for You* by B. B. Vance and D. F. Miller states: "All of the forms of plants and animals that we have studied in biology produce their young from their own bodies and in no other way."[55]

Those are the facts that science has actually proved. Yet note what evolutionist E. J. Gardner, a professor of zoology, stated in *Organic Evolution and the Bible*:

"A type of spontaneous generation may have taken place in the remote past (a billion years or

"Plants and animals ... produce their young from their own bodies and in no other way." "All life derives from preceding life, ... the parent organism and its offspring are of the same kind."

more ago) from which the forms presently living
on the earth may have descended. . . .

"The possibility of the appropriate elements,
energy and suitable environment coming together
by chance seems remote, indeed, but in tremen-
dously long periods of time the 'impossible' becomes inevitable."[56]

How can such reasoning be regarded as scientific when it is contrary to known facts? It is not
scientific at all, but is blind credulity.

UPWARD FROM THE CELL

Since the single cell was so satisfactory in the
beginning, why would it evolve into more complex
forms of life? Also, when we consider that single-
celled organisms, such as the amoeba, are still with
us today, unchanged, what would explain why
some of them evolved upward while others did
not?

If a single cell can be compared with an electronic computer, what of the complex life forms
that contain thousands of millions of cells, all
performing interrelated functions that no machine
can duplicate? Under a picture of a complicated
electronic device, *Science Year* of 1965 said:

"A spider appears to be one of nature's simpler
creatures and a spider web seems to be a simple
structure, wonderful in its symmetry. The fact is,
that the spider and its web are far more complex
than the machine above, with its tangle of wires
and electronic 'brain' . . .

"In observing nature, scientists are confronted
with the simple and the complex. And nothing
appears to be more complex than life itself."[57]

Why would a simple form of life initiate a new
organ, such as an eye? How could it know that
an eye would be an improvement when it had
never seen before? How could it know that sight
was even possible? The eye is made up of many

delicate, complicated connecting parts, such as the cornea, pupil, iris, retina, optic nerves, muscles and veins. All of these would have had to evolve simultaneously or the eye would be of no use. A partial eye would be a serious disadvantage. Darwin admitted:

> "To suppose that the eye with all its inimitable contrivances for adjusting the focus to different distances, for admitting different amounts of light, and for the correction of spherical and chromatic aberration, could have been formed by natural selection, seems, I freely confess, absurd in the highest degree."[58]

Darwin tried to explain that evolution produced the eye by many small transitional stages. Evolutionists today say it was by trial and error, and as one small transition proved advantageous it was passed along and built upon by later ones. But re-

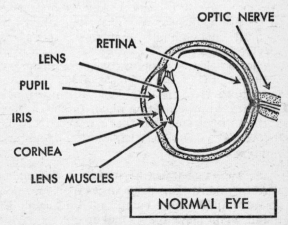

OPTIC NERVE

RETINA

LENS

PUPIL

IRIS

CORNEA

LENS MUSCLES

NORMAL EYE

If the eye evolved, its many intricate parts had to evolve simultaneously, to be of any use at all. But a camera, elementary by comparison, needed a designer and maker

gardless of what kind of creature we examine, wherever there is an eye, it is complete, and not in a transitional stage of development.

The facts about living things produce a host of other difficulties. One-celled organisms such as the amoeba reproduce asexually, that is, by themselves. They divide in two and form in duplicate. If asexual reproduction was satisfactory, and it was, because such organisms are still with us today multiplying in exactly the same way, then why would sexual reproduction arise? How could male and female sex organs that perfectly complement each other arise gradually, paralleling each other, yet useless until completed?

If the mammary glands in females came about by slow evolution, how did these females feed their offspring in the meantime? If they already had another way to feed them, then why develop breasts? And if breasts were developed because they were a superior way of feeding, then why do we still have animals that feed otherwise and survive just as well?

The complexity of multi-celled organisms caused evolutionist G. S. Carter to say in his book *Animal Evolution:* "No one can look at the immensely complicated organisation of an insect or a vertebrate without doubting that our relatively simple theories can completely explain the origin of such complexity."[59]

WHAT IS MADE REQUIRES A MAKER

All of man's knowledge and experience demonstrate that the more complicated a mechanism is the more intelligent is its maker.

We even attribute very crude instruments to a maker. When we see an old Indian arrowhead in a museum, do we ever say, "It evolved"? Do we not acknowledge that it was made by someone? Would anyone declare that a space satellite in orbit around the earth got there when a chance coordination of metal molecules formed a capsule on earth, which just happened to be connected to an evolved rocket and fuel tank, and that all of this just chanced to go into perfect orbit without any directing intelligence? We acknowledge a maker of it.

Would anyone claim that complicated mathematical formulas evolved without the intelligence of the mathematician? Could they ever be attributed to a chance coordination of chalk molecules on a blackboard? Then what of the fantastic mathematical precision found in creation? A professor of mathematics from the University of Cambridge, P. Dirac, said in *Scientific American* of May 1963:

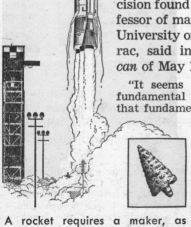

A rocket requires a maker, as does even a simple arrowhead. What of the most complex things of all—living organisms?

"It seems to be one of the fundamental features of nature that fundamental physical laws are described in terms of a mathematical theory of great beauty and power, needing quite a high standard of mathematics for one to understand it. . . . One could perhaps describe the situation by saying that God is a mathematician of a very high order, and He used very advanced mathematics in constructing the universe."[60]

Is a mathematics formula ever the result of a chance coordination of chalk molecules on a blackboard?

That what is made requires a maker was interestingly demonstrated once by Sir Isaac Newton, the British scientist. Once he had a skillful mechanic make him a miniature replica of our solar system, with balls representing the planets geared together by cogs and belts so as to move in harmony when cranked. Later, Newton was visited by a scientist friend who did not believe in God. Their conversation is related in the *Minnesota Technolog*:

"One day, as Newton sat reading in his study with his mechanism on a large table near him, his infidel friend stepped in. Scientist that he was, he recognized at a glance what was before him. Stepping up to it, he slowly turned the crank, and with undisguised admiration watched the heavenly bodies all move in their relative speed in their orbits. Standing off a few feet he exclaimed, 'My! What an exquisite thing this is!

Who made it?' Without looking up from his book, Newton answered, 'Nobody!'

"Quickly turning to Newton, the infidel said, 'Evidently you did not understand my question. I asked who made this?' Looking up now, Newton solemnly assured him that nobody made it, but that the aggregation of matter so much admired had just happened to assume the form it was in. But the astonished infidel replied with some heat, 'You must think I am a fool! Of course somebody made it, and he is a genius, and I'd like to know who he is.'

"Laying his book aside, Newton arose and laid a hand on his friend's shoulder. 'This thing is but a puny imitation of a much grander system whose laws you know, and I am not able to convince you that this mere toy is without a designer and maker; yet you profess to believe that the great original from which the design is taken has come into being without either designer or maker! Now tell me by what sort of reasoning do you reach such an incongruous conclusion?' "[61]

How much of it evolved by itself? How much is the result of an intelligent maker?

Newton convinced his friend that whatever is made requires a maker. If we but look about us in our daily lives, the same conclusion is forced upon us time and again. When you are in your room, ask yourself, How much of it came about by evolution, and how much as the result of an intelligent maker? Did your desk evolve by itself or did it require a maker? What of your lamp, bed, chair, stove, table, rug, wall, or even the building itself? All these things required a maker! Even you had to have a mother and father! By what reasoning, then, can it be claimed that the most complex things of all, living things, did not require a maker?

The logical conclusion based on all the facts is that drawn by one research chemist who wrote:

> "So highly intricate are the organic and bio-chemical processes functioning in the animal organism, that it is not surprising that malfunction and disease occasionally intervene. One is rather amazed that a mechanism of such intricacy could ever function properly at all. All this demands a planner and sustainer of infinite intelligence. . . . The simplest man-made mechanism requires a planner and a maker. How a mechanism ten thousand times more involved and intricate can be conceived of as self-constructed and self-developed is completely beyond me."[62]

While admitting the logic of such conclusions, many still maintain that evolution must have taken place, and they point to the fossils that have been found in the earth as proof of evolution. But are they proof in actuality?

CHAPTER 4

What Does the Fossil Record Show?

IF LIVING things evolved from one-celled organisms into higher forms of animal and plant life, then we would expect to see evidence of this in the fossil record. Surely some of those earliest forms left either their fossils, their imprints, or other evidences in the earth. What does the fossil record show?

Over a century ago the record disturbed even Charles Darwin. He wrote of this in his book *The Origin of Species:*

> "There is another and allied difficulty, which is much more serious. I allude to the manner in which species belonging to several of the main divisions of the animal kingdom suddenly appear in the lowest known fossiliferous rocks. . . .

> "If the [evolution] theory be true, it is indisputable that before the lowest Cambrian stratum was deposited long periods elapsed, as long as, or probably far longer than, the whole interval from the Cambrian age to the present day; and that during these vast periods the world swarmed with living creatures. . . .

> "To the question why we do not find rich fossiliferous deposits belonging to these assumed earliest periods prior to the Cambrian system, I can give no satisfactory answer. . . . the difficulty of assigning any good reason for the absence of vast piles of strata rich in fossils beneath the Cambrian system is very great."[63]

The Cambrian layer of earth mentioned by Darwin is said, by evolutionists, to be about 600,000,-000 years old. In Darwin's day the fossil record of the pre-Cambrian layers was a blank. Now, after more than a hundred years of intensive investigation, what do the facts show? The New York *Times* of October 25, 1964, in an article supporting evolution, admits that that period is still a blank:

"The chief puzzle in the record of life's history on earth: the sudden appearance, some 600 million years ago, of most basic divisions of the plant and animal kingdoms. There is virtually no record of how these divisions came about. Thus the entire first part of evolutionary history is missing."[64]

The same admission is made by the book *The World We Live In:* "For at least three-quarters of the book of ages engraved in the earth's crust the pages are blank."[65]

Note also what *Scientific American* of August 1964 says:

"Both the sudden appearance and the remarkable composition of the animal life characteristic of Cambrian times are sometimes explained away or overlooked by biologists. Yet recent paleontological research has made the puzzle of this sudden proliferation of living organisms increasingly difficult for anyone to evade. . . .

"These animals were neither primitive nor generalized in anatomy: they were complex organisms that clearly belonged to the various distinct phyla, or major groups of animals, now classified as metazoan. In fact, they are now known to include representatives of nearly every major phylum that possessed skeletal structures capable of fossilization; . . .

"Yet before the Lower Cambrian there is scarcely a trace of them. The appearance of the Lower Cambrian fauna . . . can reasonably be called a 'sudden' event.

"One can no longer dismiss this event by assuming that all Pre-Cambrian rocks have been too greatly altered by time to allow the fossils ancestral to the Cambrian metazoans to be preserved. . . . even if all the Pre-Cambrian ancestors of the Cambrian metazoans were similarly soft-bodied and therefore rarely preserved, far more abundant traces of their activities should have been found in the Pre-Cambrian strata than has proved to be the case. Neither can the general failure to find Pre-Cambrian animal fossils be charged to any lack of trying."[66]

These same conclusions are drawn in *Natural History* magazine of October 1959 in an article entitled "Darwin and the Fossil Record":

"From the beginning of the Cambrian up through the rest of the geological sequence, we have an abundant representation of animal life at every stage; even in Lower Cambrian formations, marine invertebrates are numerous and varied. Below this, there are vast thicknesses of sediments in which the progenitors of the Cambrian forms should be expected. But we do not find them; these older beds are almost barren of evidence of life, and the general picture could reasonably be said to be consistent with the idea of a special creation at the beginning of Cambrian times.

" 'To the question why we do not find rich fossiliferous deposits belonging to these assumed earliest periods prior to the Cambrian system,' said Darwin, 'I can give no satisfactory answer.' Nor can we today."

How is this fact explained away? The evolutionists who made this last admission stated: "The objection is based merely on negative evidence, which experience often shows to be worthless."[67] In other words, although evolutionists find no pre-Cambrian fossils, the record being "three-quarters . . . blank," they contend that evolution took place anyway because the total lack of evidence is merely "negative evidence."

Such a conclusion is utterly unscientific. The scientific method of finding truth is to support conclusions with facts, and when they are lacking, to reject the conclusions. Further showing the determination of evolutionists to hold their conclusions despite a lack of supporting facts is a subtitle in this same article that says: "In the century since Darwin's controversial theory first appeared, paleontologists have established a solid foundation for evolution."[68] But then the article goes on to show, as already noted, that the majority of the fossil record needed for the theory is completely devoid of facts and evidence!

Can this, except by sheer credulity, be called "a solid foundation" for the theory? What would you think if a builder told you he had built a solid foundation for a building, but, upon investigating, you found there was nothing at all, no concrete, no steel, no wood, no supporting material of any kind, just empty space where the strong foundation should have been? Would you consider such a void "a solid foundation" for a building because it was just "negative evidence"?

No, we cannot escape the scientific facts regarding this matter. The fossil record of the earth supports a sudden creation, not a slow evolution from primitive forms of life.

WHERE ARE THE LINKS?

About three-quarters of the evolutionary chain is missing. But what about the fossils that have been found? Do they provide the needed evidence for proving evolution? Does the fossil record supply the links at least in the last quarter of the evolutionary chain? Let us consider the facts.

Regarding so-called links, Charles Darwin stated:

> "Why, if species have descended from other species by fine gradations, do we not everywhere see innumerable transitional forms? Why is not all nature in confusion, instead of the species being, as we see them, well defined?"

> "But, as by this [evolution] theory innumerable transitional forms must have existed, why do we not find them embedded in countless numbers in the crust of the earth?"

> "Geological research . . . does not yield the infinitely many fine gradations between past and present species required."[69]

How did Darwin explain this lack of links? He declared: "I believe the answer lies in the record being incomparably less perfect than is generally supposed."[70] But then, in a later chapter, he says: "If we confine our attention to any one formation, it becomes much more difficult to understand why we do not therein find closely graduated varieties between the allied species."[71]

Has this picture changed in the years since Darwin's time? Have links between major groups of living things been found in the fossil record? Note what the world-famous evolutionary scholar George Gaylord Simpson of Harvard University said in his book *The Major Features of Evolution:*

> "It remains true, as every paleontologist knows, that *most* new species, genera, and families and that nearly all new categories above the level of families appear in the record suddenly and are not led up to by known, gradual, completely continuous transitional sequences."[72]

The same fact is noted by A. S. Romer, zoology professor from Harvard University. Writing in the book *Genetics, Paleontology and Evolution,* edited by prominent evolutionists Glenn L. Jepsen, Ernst Mayr and George Gaylord Simpson, he says:

> "In rapid evolutionary changes in animal lines the process may have been a typically Neo-Darwinian one of the accumulation of numerous small adaptive mutations, but an accumulation at an unusually rapid rate. Unfortunately there is in general little evidence on this point in the fossil record, for intermediate evolutionary forms representative of this phenomenon are extremely rare."

> " 'Links' are missing just where we most fervently desire them, and it is all too probable that many 'links' will continue to be missing."[73]

Concerning this matter of links Professor D'Arcy Thompson once said in his book *On Growth and Form*:

> "Eighty years' study of Darwinian evolution has not taught us how birds descend from reptiles, mammals from earlier quadrupeds, quadrupeds from fishes, nor vertebrates from the invertebrate stock. The invertebrates themselves involve the selfsame difficulties, . . . the breach between vertebrate and invertebrate, worm and coelenterate, coelenterate and protozoan, . . . is so wide that we cannot see across the intervening gap at all. . . .

> "We cross a boundary every time we pass from family to family, or group to group. . . .

> "A 'principle of discontinuity,' then, is inherent in all our classifications, . . . to seek for stepping stones across the gaps between is to seek in vain for ever."[74]

The same facts confront us in regard to plant life. Dr. Heribert Nilsson, professor of botany from the University of Lund, Sweden, said in his book *Synthetic Speciation*:

> "If we look at the peculiar main groups of the fossil flora, it is quite striking that at definite intervals of geological time they are all at once

and quite suddenly there, and, moreover, in full bloom in all their manifold forms. And it is quite as surprising that after a time which is to be measured not only in millions, but in tens of millions of years, *they disappear equally suddenly*. Furthermore, at the end of their existence they do not change into forms which are transitional towards the main types of the next period: such are entirely lacking."[75]

Not only are there no transitional forms between major groups of animals and plants in the *fossil* record, but there are no transitional forms among major groups of *living* plants and animals today. Professor Dobzhansky, famous evolutionist from Columbia University, in his book *Genetics and the Origin of Species* declared:

"If we assemble as many individuals living at a given time as we can, we notice at once that the observed variation does not form any kind of continuous distribution. Instead, a multitude of separate, discrete, distributions are found. The living world is not a single array in which any two variants are connected by unbroken series of intergrades, but an array of more or less distinctly separate arrays, intermediates between which are absent or at least rare."[76]

Among man's supposedly closest relatives, the ape family, there are no living transitional stages to man; nor can there be seen living transitional steps to the apes; nor can even the apes' supposed evolutionary ancestors be found in the fossil record. The book *The Primates* said in 1965:

"Unfortunately, the fossil record which would enable us to trace the emergence of the apes is still hopelessly incomplete. We do not know either when or where distinctively apelike animals first began to diverge from monkey stock."[77]

However, some persons claim that at least the horse provides a classic example in the fossil record of transitional stages upward. Evolutionists begin with *Eohippus*, a small, foxlike animal, and place after it a series of progressively larger fossils up to the modern horse. The actual fact is that not even in one place is this order found in the fossil record. Two or even three horse types may occur in the same formation. Some are found at widely separated localities.

Of horse evolution a headline in *Science News Letter* declared: "Little Eohippus Not Direct Ancestor of the Horse." It commented:

> "The ancestral family tree of the horse is not what scientists have thought it to be. Prof. T. S. Westoll, Durham University geologist, told the British Association for the Advancement of Science at Edinburgh that the early classical evolutionary tree of the horse, beginning in the small dog-sized Eohippus and tracing directly to our present day Equinus, was all wrong."[78]

Of the series of fossils placed between *Eohippus* and the modern horse, evolutionist Lecomte du Noüy wrote in *Human Destiny:*

> "Each one of these intermediaries seems to have appeared 'suddenly,' and it has not yet been possible, because of the lack of fossils, to reconstitute the passage between these intermediaries. . . . The known forms remain separated like the piers of a ruined bridge . . . The continuity we surmise may never be established by facts."[79]

Where, then, are all the "in between" stages or links of the evolutionary chain in either the fossil record or in the record of living things today? Why is it always the same story, that the transitions, the links between major groups of plants and animals, are missing? Why do the major groups of complex organisms always appear suddenly, separated by structural gaps from members of other groups? Why are such things as arms, legs, eyes and wings always found to be completely developed? If evolution were true, there simply had to be various stages of development in different limbs and organs. But such stages are never found.

These hard facts distress evolutionists. When G. G. Simpson wrote in *Science* magazine about the book *The Origin of Vertebrates* by N. J. Berrill, he said: "Berrill's last sentence is, 'Proof may be for ever unobtainable, and it may not matter, for here is such stuff as dreams are made on.'" Then Simpson himself stated: "*Perhaps* this is the last word on the chordate ancestry of the vertebrates. As for the ancestry of the chordates, all is left in darkness without even the dream of 60 years ago."[80]

For evolution to be true, there had to be thousands, millions of transitional forms making an unbroken chain. The lack of these transitional forms in the fossil record, or among living things for that matter, makes it an imaginary chain without connecting links. Instead of links, the fossil record shows that groups of plants and animals are always differentiated. Why is that the fact we find in the fossil record? Why are groups of plants and animals always separate and distinct from one another?

CHAPTER 5

Fundamental Law
of All Living Things

THERE exists a law among all living things that has no exception, a law that science has clearly verified. As noted by *Scientific American* of December 1966: "Living things are enormously diverse in form, but form is remarkably constant within any given line of descent: pigs remain pigs and oak trees remain oak trees generation after generation."[81]

The law involved here is mentioned in the first book of the Bible, the book of Genesis. There it states:

"And the earth began to put forth grass, vegetation bearing seed *according to its kind* and trees yielding fruit, the seed of which is in it *according to its kind.* . . . great sea monsters and every living soul that moves about, which the waters swarmed forth *according to their kinds,* and every winged flying creature *according to its kind.* . . . the wild beast of the earth *according to its kind* and the domestic animal *according to its kind* and every moving animal of the ground *according to its kind.*"—Genesis 1:12, 21, 25.

The fixity of basic *kinds* of living things as stated here is an unchangeable law on earth. That is just what science has found, that there are basic animal and plant groupings and between these there are no links. Each group multiplies and has offspring within itself but cannot reproduce when crossed with other major groups.

But when the Bible speaks of God as creating various kinds of life on earth, it does not mean every single species known to man. In the system of nomenclature used in the life sciences, individual organisms very closely related are considered a *species*. One or more related species make up a *genus*. A *family* is a group of genera (plural of genus). An example is that of the cat family, *Felidae*. One genus of this family is *Felis,* which includes the tiger, lion, house cat and others, all separate species within the genus. Another genus of the cat family is the *Lynx,* which includes the bobcat. Further classification upward into *order, class* and then *phylum* follow.

Which of all these classifications commonly used today is the equivalent of the Genesis *kind?* The Bible does not say, but the kind to which it refers is large enough to allow for great variety within but not for interbreeding with other kinds. Observed facts prove this to be so. That is why there are no transitional stages between major groups, either in the fossil record or among living things today. A century of careful investigation in this matter of classification has revealed that any "new" types that spring up now are not really "new" but are merely varieties within the basic Genesis kinds already existing.

For the sake of discussion, let us refer to the *family* classification. All in the cat family remain always cats, in fossil form or those living today. There is great variety in the cat family, lions, tigers, leopards, bobcats, house cats, and so forth, but they always remain cats. All in the dog family have always remained in that family, again allowing for great variety, such as domestic dogs, jackals, wolves, foxes and others.

So when we look at the cat family or the dog family and see various sizes, shapes and colors, this is not organic evolution, but merely variety within a basic Genesis kind. There is great diversity within a kind, but the kinds have never, and do not now, mix. Not a single shred of evidence indicates that the basic kinds ever evolved from a common ancestor. There are no facts from which to conclude that they did as evolution claims.

Even with the classification listed lower than *family,* that is, *genus,* there are marked differences. And even of *species* Professor Dobzhansky comments:

> "No individual has ever been seen about which there could be a doubt as to whether it belongs to the species of cats (*Felis domestica*) or to the species of lions (*Felis leo*). The two species are discrete because of the absence of intermediates. Therefore, one may safely affirm that any cat is different from any lion. . . .
>
> "What has been said above with respect to the species *Felis domestica* and *Felis leo* holds for innumerable other pairs of species. Discrete groups are encountered among animals as well as plants, among structurally simple as well as among very complex ones. Formation of discrete groups is so nearly universal that it must be regarded as a fundamental characteristic of organic diversity."[82]

So while it cannot be said with certainty which modern classification is the same as the Genesis kind, it was a category that had definite physiological differences that made it impossible for the germ cells of one kind to unite with the germ cells of another kind and produce offspring. Thus, the amoeba stayed forever an amoeba, a fly stayed forever a fly, and an ape stayed forever an ape.

REPRODUCTION ONLY "ACCORDING TO ITS KIND"

CAT

DOG

A cat and a dog cannot mate and produce offspring together because they are of different "kinds"

HORSE   DONKEY   MULE

A horse and a donkey can produce the hybrid mule, but the mule is sterile. It has reached the limits of its "kind"

All varieties of humans are fertile with one another. The smallest and the tallest can mate, as can those of different races, because all humans belong to the same "kind"

SMALLEST   TALLEST

That these are the facts science has verified, Professor of Zoology Richard B. Goldschmidt, a famous evolutionist, once said in his book *The Material Basis of Evolution:* "The facts fail to give any information regarding the origin of actual species, not to mention higher categories." He added: "Nowhere have the limits of the species been transgressed, and these limits are separated from the limits of the next good species by the unbridged gap, which also includes sterility."[83]

HYBRIDS

However, are not hybrids proof of the crossing of different Genesis kinds? Of hybrids *Biology for Today* states:

> "In the process of hybridization, two different species of the same genus (in most cases) are crossed in order to combine the good qualities of both . . . Frequently the new hybrid is stronger than either parent. Sometimes the offspring are sterile and require constant hybridizing."[84]

Note the point that hybrids come from living things closely related to begin with, which means they are likely in the same Genesis kind all the time. Many of these hybrids are sterile, and in the free state usually do not even breed. And with those that may be fertile, further hybridizing reaches a final limit, sterility. Hence, variability, although great, is definitely limited within a kind, not unlimited as evolutionists assume.

This limitation can be seen in working with hybrid corn. For several decades phenomenal progress was made in raising high-yield hybrid corn. But then the hybrid corn seed could not be significantly improved in yield, because all the factors for improving this particular characteristic had been utilized. Also, no matter what was done to that corn, it always stayed corn. It did not, and can not, change into some other kind of plant. All the changes it ever experiences will be made within its basic kind. This is also true of animal hybrids. Efforts to change them indefinitely will always prove futile, as they soon reach the boundary of sterility, which boundary cannot be crossed. This keeps basic kinds always separate.

ADAPTATION

Various species of plants and animals have adapted to different circumstances, such as climatic changes. Is this evidence of evolution? No, because plants and animals are not first non-adapted and then become adapted. They already have within their organisms the possibility of lesser or greater adaptation. The cactus did not evolve into

Although preferring a cold climate, the polar bear can adapt to warmer weather. This capacity for adaptation is part of its hereditary makeup, not evolution

a cactus from a different plant just because the climate became dry. Some features may become accentuated in severe climatic changes, but that possibility of variation was there to begin with.

Did the polar bear evolve to become a cold weather animal? No, for it can survive in warmer climates too, as it does in many zoos throughout the world. But it had the capacity to adapt to cold weather better than other animals. Such is the case with all animals and plants that seem particularly adapted to local conditions. In regard to adaptability, evolutionist Dobzhansky comments:

> "The English sparrow introduced in the United States from Europe has changed detectably in its new home; the average size of the birds has increased, and they became differentiated into incipient local races."[85]

What is proved by the English sparrow in the United States becoming larger? Only that it had the potential of change already present in it. But that sparrow continues to be a sparrow. It does not change into another kind of animal, and never will. Adaptability is confused with evolution.

Evolutionist De Beer cites another example as proof of evolution. Under a picture of a woodpecker, his book states:

> "The woodpecker has two toes on each foot pointing backward, enabling it to get a firm foothold on the bark of trees, stiff tail feathers serving to prop it securely against the tree, a long stout beak with which it chisels holes in the bark, and a very long tongue with which it reaches and takes the grubs at the bottoms of the holes. . . . these adaptations must have arisen during the evolution of the woodpecker."[86]

PRIME EXAMPLE OF EVOLUTION?

| Light form of peppered moth | Dark form of peppered moth |

The peppered moth in Britain is often used as a prime example of evolution. It is claimed that within the last 100 years the moth evolved from the light color to the dark color in order to be better camouflaged against a background turned dark by industrial pollution, thus protecting it against birds.

However, has organic evolution occurred? Is the moth changing into something else? Is it evolving into a more complex organism? Or is it still a moth, remaining in the moth "kind"?

Indeed, no evolution has taken place at all, as can be seen by comparing the two varieties illustrated above. The dark variety is a moth just as is the light variety. No matter which variety survives better, they do not change into a different kind of organism. They always remain moths.

Once again, variety within a basic kind of living thing has been misinterpreted as organic evolution. In fact, none has taken place.

However, what was the woodpecker doing to survive before it got its backward toes, long beak and tongue? If it survived for a time with a different foot, shorter beak and tongue, as so many other birds have, then why develop these other features? And if such other equipment was necessary for survival under new conditions, how did all the rest of the shorter-beaked birds get by? The fact that birds of all kinds, gathering food in different ways, live side by side today and survive shows that they were made with certain characteristics and could adjust, to a certain extent, to changing environment. It does not at all mean they evolved for advantage.

If different feeding habits are attributed to evolution, enabling some to survive better than

Horse has upper front teeth

Cow lacks upper front teeth

Both horse and cow eat the same food, exist side by side, survive equally well. Why would one evolve with upper front teeth, the other without them?

others, then what would we say of the cow and horse, both eating the same grass in the same meadow? Why did one evolve with upper front teeth and the other without them? How could both exist side by side, each better suited for survival, one because it had those teeth, and the other because it did not?

Another instance of adaptability that is confused with evolution is that which occurred when flies were exposed to the insecticide DDT. For a while DDT proved very effective, killing most of the flies it contacted. But some flies were able to resist DDT. They survived and reproduced offspring that were also resistant. But they were still flies. What had happened was not evolution, but some flies had greater resistance, greater adaptability, to DDT than others.

The capacity to adapt can change appearances in living things. Of that there is no doubt. But that change is never so large that a totally new kind is formed no matter how long a time is involved.

Do Mutations Result in New Life Forms?

A CENTRAL point, a foundation, to the entire theory of organic evolution is the belief that small mutations caused the changes that resulted in the slow transition of one form of life into another. What are the facts in this regard? Are mutations helpful? Do they ever result in new forms of life?

The word "mutation" is from the Latin *mutare,* meaning "to change." A mutation is an inheritable change, an alteration within the germ plasm of the cell. As Dobzhansky states: "Mutation produces changes in the genes and variants of the gene structure; these are the raw materials of evolution."[87] In the book *The New You and Heredity* A. Scheinfeld adds:

> "It is through the rare instances of favorable mutations, of innumerable kinds and in countless numbers, occurring successively over very extended periods, that the whole process of evolution may now be explained."[88]

Why do mutations occur? *Biology for Today* says: "Mutations probably occur due to factors normally found in the environment: cosmic rays and other ionizing radiations; metabolic processes in cells; or errors in gene replication."[89]

Do mutations occur frequently? In the book

Radiation, Genes and Man by Professors B. Wallace and T. Dobzhansky we read: "Mutational changes in any one gene are rare events. This is a different way of saying that, ordinarily, the genes reproduce themselves accurately."[90] In *Science Today* evolutionist C. H. Waddington says: "It happens rarely, perhaps once in a million animals or once in a million lifetimes."[91] The 1966 *World Book Encyclopedia* says: "Mutations rarely occur. Most genes mutate only once in 100,000 generations or more." This source also states: "Researchers estimate that a human gene may remain stable for 2,500,000 years."

However, this encyclopedia also says: "Most mutations are harmful. Some make it impossible for the cells in which they occur to develop and grow."[92] Is this actually the case? Are most of the comparatively few mutations that do occur harmful?

Over the past few decades many experiments have been conducted to determine the characteristics of mutations. Particularly has this been so of the common fruit fly, *Drosophila melanogaster,* beginning with the work of T. H. Morgan (1866-1945) at Columbia University. Others, such as H. J. Muller, continued this work. Muller received the Nobel prize in 1946 for his contributions in this field.

The results of all this experimentation are clear, definite. Muller himself said: "Most mutations are bad, in fact good ones are so rare that we may consider them all as bad."[93] Dowdeswell in *The Mechanism of Evolution* also acknowledges: "Of the many mutants detected in the laboratory, all are either recessives or 'semi-dominants,' and the majority cause harmful physiological effects. Hardly any have ever been observed which could possibly be beneficial to an organism under wild conditions."[94] Dobzhansky also admits:

"A majority of mutations, both those arising in laboratories and those stored in natural populations, produce deteriorations of the viability, hereditary diseases, and monstrosities. Such changes, it would seem, can hardly serve as evolutionary building blocks."[95]

Horticultural expert Dr. W. E. Lammerts comments on the results of his work with roses:

"My own work on neutron radiation of roses describes a technique by which we can induce 50 radiated buds of Queen Elizabeth, more mutations than could hitherto be found in a lifetime of searching among several million rose plants grown annually from non-radiated buds. Without exception, all mutations induced were found to be defective or weaker than Queen Elizabeth. . . . biologically they would hardly compete because of reduced vigor and partial sterility."[96]

A report in the New Zealand *Herald* of January 17, 1963, stated: "Whether the mutations are natural or induced by some artificial means such as radiation . . . the evidence today suggests that much more than 99 percent of mutations are undesirable."[97]

Professor H. J. Muller similarly stated this. In an article entitled "Radiation and Human Mutation" in *Scientific American* of November 1955 he said: "In more than 99 per cent of cases the mutation of a gene produces some kind of harmful effect, some disturbance of function."[98]

In the 1963 book *Progress and Decline* Professor Hugh Miller says:

"The relative rarity of these aberrant or mutant changes, together with their usually maladaptive and more often than not lethal effects upon development, does not incline us to assign to them an important role in the maintenance of group-adaptability. . . . It should be observed that the great importance currently attached to gene-mutations as a factor in evolutionary history is in part the result of erroneous expectations initially aroused by their discovery."[99]

The germ plasm of living things is in delicate balance, so that any disruption is almost sure to be in the direction of disorganization. A striking example of this occurred in Hiroshima and Nagasaki, Japan. Atomic bombs that exploded over these cities in 1945 caused many mutations. None were beneficial and so could not be regarded as an aid to further the cause of evolution. Many resulted in damage, deformity or death. That is why great precautions are taken by research workers to protect themselves from radiation.

Chemicals, too, can cause mutations, as we saw in the use of the tranquilizer drug thalidomide. Were the mutations that resulted from its use beneficial? To the contrary, they produced horribly deformed babies, some without arms or legs.

Chemicals have caused fish to develop, not two eyes, but a single median eye. Is the one-eyed fish better suited for survival? Is it not, instead, just a freak that is ill suited for survival as compared with its normal counterparts? Siamese twins are mutants. Are they regarded as having a better chance to survive than normal humans? Two-headed fish have been collected in fish hatcheries, but observers are informed that they would soon die if released in the streams, as the mutation has made them inferior, poorly suited for survival.

Many other mutations have been induced by experimentation. There are featherless chickens; insects having eyes with colors different than usual; changes in the size of wings and other limbs in various organisms. But in the free state, few, if any, of such mutations confer advantages.

Mutations are compared with accidents in the genetic machinery of living things. They are more like the wrecking of an automobile, not the building of one. An accident is not associated with improvement, but with disaster. Dropping a delicate watch or throwing a wrench into a computer's mechanism is not calculated to improve performance.

An appeal to immense spans of time, millions of years, does not change the picture. What was impossible yesterday and is impossible today will be impossible tomorrow in this regard. If an automobile accident yesterday did not produce improvement in its mechanism, is it likely to do so today or tomorrow? And even if we were to grant that one out of 100 accidents *might* improve the automobile, what of the following 99 accidents that will be harmful? How much will be left after 99 harmful accidents? If it is functioning

Does an accident improve the automobile or transform it into a higher type? Mutations are likened to accidents in the genetic machinery, and "good ones are so rare that we may consider them all as bad"

at all, it will still be an automobile, but an inferior one.

With living things it is the same. Over a great span of time the line of the organism will be injured by the 99 harmful mutations, making it less suited for survival. Even if it did survive through many generations it would only be a weaker species. And certainly it will not have turned into a new kind of life.

This brings us to another fact that must be considered: Not one of the thousands of experiments with mutations has ever resulted in the production of a new *kind* of animal or plant. Mutational changes always remain within the basic Genesis *kind* to which the plant or animal belongs. All the many mutations induced in *Drosophila* produced only fruit flies belonging to the same *kind* as their ancestors. While their sizes, shapes and colors were varied, no mutation or series of mutations ever resulted in a different organism.

The truth of the entire matter concerning mutations is as was stated in *The Bible and Modern Science:*

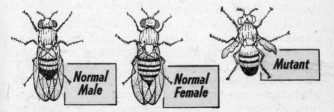

Normal Male   Normal Female   Mutant

The many mutations induced in fruit flies produced only fruit flies of the same "kind" as the parent organisms. Sizes, shapes and colors were altered, as in the mutant above, but the mutations never resulted in a new "kind"

"When one considers the great odds against a mutation's being helpful and surviving in the struggle for existence and then realizes that the formation of a new species would require not one mutation but thousands, and finally considers the tremendous number of species of plants and animals in the world, it would seem to demand a most amazing credulity to imagine that here is the method by which evolution takes place. And yet that is precisely what is taught as gospel truth in probably the majority of schools today."[100]

Considering all the facts impartially, one arrives at the logical conclusion that mutations are not at all evolutionary in nature but are degenerative. Interestingly, *The Encyclopædia Britannica,* although supporting evolution, admitted: "Although combinations, reshufflings and duplications of existing genes may give rise to many mutations, they can hardly account for the vast changes which have taken place in organic evolution."[101]

"NATURAL SELECTION"

There is no favorable trend of mutations, but, instead, there is an unfavorable trend, a downward, degenerative trend. What, then, does this fact do to the other part of the modern theory, that is, the part called "natural selection"?

In his book *Charles Darwin* De Beer writes: "Natural selection . . . controls evolution."[102] It is claimed that "nature" keeps "selecting" beneficial mutations and rejecting harmful ones, so that one kind of life eventually becomes another, improved kind. But since "more than 99 per cent" of mutations are harmful, what is there for "nature" to "select"? If an organism did have a beneficial mutation (which is highly questionable), but then this same line had a host of harmful mutations, "nature," if it did anything, would reject this organism because it would be inferior. "Natural selection" would actually be the enemy of evolution, just as mutations are.

"Natural selection" or "survival of the fittest" never produces anything *new*. Because a living thing has survived, that does not mean it evolved. If a hen hatches a dozen chicks, and some are killed by predators, does that indicate they evolved? No, all it indicates is that some chicks survived while the others died. This "selection" by "nature" in no way changes the chick to something new.

Evolutionists themselves even express dissatisfaction with the combination of mutations and natural selection as being the mechanism of evolution. In the book *Science Today* confirmed evolutionist Sir James Gray said:

> "All biologists are not equally satisfied. Some feel that the argument gets uncomfortably close to a point when an adequate number of monkeys, tapping typewriters for an adequate length of time will inevitably produce an encyclopedia. Such a thing, of course, is conceivably possible but nobody in their senses takes such things into consideration in everyday life."

> "We either have to accept natural selection as the only available guide to the mechanism of evolution, and be prepared to admit that it involves a considerable element of speculation, or feel in our bones that natural selection, operating on the random mutations, leaves too much to chance. . . . If we look on organic evolution as one of Nature's games of chance it seems just a little strange that she should have dealt quite so many winning hands. But, your guess is as good as mine."[103]

In the same book evolutionist C. H. Waddington, a professor of animal genetics from Edinburgh University, said of mutations and natural selection:

> "This is really the theory that if you start with any fourteen lines of coherent English and change it one letter at a time, keeping only those things that still make sense, you will eventually finish up with one of the sonnets of Shakespeare. . . . it strikes me as a lunatic sort of logic, and I think we should be able to do better."[104]

And remember what evolutionary biologist Rostand said:

> "No, decidedly, I cannot make myself think that these 'slips' of heredity have been able, even with the cooperation of natural selection, even with the advantage of the immense periods of time in which evolution works on life, to build the entire world, with its structural prodigality and refinements, its astounding 'adaptations.' "[105]

It is little wonder that in his 1965 book *The Geography of Evolution* George Gaylord Simpson, the renowned evolutionist, said: "Search for *the* cause of evolution has been abandoned. It is now clear that evolution has no single or simple cause."[106]

Does all of this sound like evidence for the "fact" of evolution? Most assuredly not. No, at best "natural selection" or "survival of the fittest" can only mean separating the strong from the weak. But a new kind of plant or a new kind of animal is never the result of survival alone. And since new kinds of living things do not result from mutations either, evolution is left completely without a mechanism that could account for it.

CHAPTER 7

Heredity Keeps
Family Kinds Separate

S CIENCE is now unraveling one of the most amazing facts of all concerning heredity. It helps to account for the fact that neither mutations nor "natural selection" nor any other factor proposed by advocates of evolution could result in the forming of a different kind of life from a previous kind.

Science now has a clearer understanding of the mechanism that is so precise that it fulfills continually the Genesis law of reproduction only "after its kind." It has to do with the substance called DNA, a shortened name for deoxyribonucleic acid. DNA has been found to be the carrier of the inheritance code in living things.

DNA is like a microscopic computer with a built-in memory. It stores a fantastic number of "blueprints" and at the right time and place issues orders to build all the cells and structures of every plant and animal. This DNA is the chemical compound of which genes are made. Science writer Rutherford Platt says of it:

"Your personal DNA is peppered throughout your body in about 60 thousand billion specks—the average number of living cells in a human adult. . . .

"Surprisingly, the DNA molecule has a basically simple form. It consists of two intertwined, tape-

69

like coils of lined-up atoms connected by cross-pieces at regular intervals—like a spiral staircase. . . . There is logic in the long slender form of DNA: this gives it a capacity, like magnetic recording tape, to store the vast amount of data needed in a lifetime.

"The DNA tapes themselves are of sugar and phosphate; the crosspieces of the spiral staircase are nitrogen compounds. . . . Their varying sequence on the DNA tapes directs the events which make bodies grow—much as the tiny variations on magnetic tapes produce, according to their order, the sounds of the music. . . .

"Dr. Beadle says that if we were to put the coded DNA instructions of a single human cell into English, they would fill a 1000-volume encyclopedia.

"All the while that DNA sits in the nucleus giving orders that will spur growth, digestion, heartbeat, thinking and feeling, it is following its built-in plan which it has carried down the corridors of time. It makes no alterations in that plan, unless they are imposed by radiations or accidents from outside the cell."[107]

So DNA constitutes a built-in code, a blueprint, a tape recording that keeps all forms of life within their basic kinds. It allows for no alterations unless they are imposed by accidents such as radiations from outside the cell. Mutations fall into this category, and as we have already seen, they do not improve, but impair the progress of an organism. The amazing DNA keeps the organism within the bounds originally set out for it, from which bounds it cannot deviate without harm. As *Scientific American* of October 1963 said:

"If the code is indeed universal, as these and other results suggest, it implies that it has been fixed throughout most of organic evolution, in other words, that it is not subject to mutation."[108]

What capacity for variety, within its kind, does DNA allow for? *Science Year* of 1966 states:

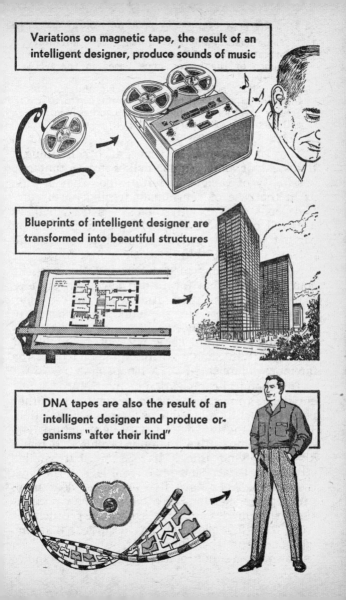

Variations on magnetic tape, the result of an intelligent designer, produce sounds of music

Blueprints of intelligent designer are transformed into beautiful structures

DNA tapes are also the result of an intelligent designer and produce organisms "after their kind"

"Geneticists have determined that hereditary information for all species is determined by the sequence of the nitrogenous bases in the DNA molecule. . . .

"A gene has 1,000 or more such units strung together in a long thread. The genes, in turn, are strung together to make a chromosome. A human cell has tens of thousands of genes grouped into 23 pairs of chromosomes."[109]

Tens of thousands of genes, each containing a thousand or more units, makes for a fantastic possibility of variety within a kind. That is why, as in the case of the human family, hardly any two people look exactly alike, even though there are well over three thousand million persons on earth today. Yet, in spite of all that variety, all persons remain within the basic human kind.

Such an amazing mechanism as DNA, with its complex blueprints for future development, is a marvel of organization. And when we see blueprints responsible for the building of beautiful bridges, buildings and machines, do we ever contend they came into being without an intelligent designer? Why should not the same be true of the far more complicated DNA blueprints?

The chemical composition of the DNA of different living things helps us to understand another point frequently alluded to as a proof for evolution. This is the matter of similarity of structure. The study of comparative anatomy reveals that many kinds of living things have somewhat similar structures. Lizards have two front legs. Birds have two wings. Apes have two arms. So does man. Line up the skeletons of each, and one can see a similarity in design. The evolutionist concludes from this that evolution has occurred, that one has come from the other.

However, a study of the DNA molecule shows

that different living creatures are basically made up of the same chemicals. As Rutherford Platt put it:

> "These DNA specks have a similar chemical composition, are about the same size, and look very much like those in your dog, or in a housefly, a bread mold or blade of grass. Yet somehow the specks are coded to make every living thing different from every other living thing. They make dogs different from fish or birds, bread mold from apple trees, elephants from mosquitoes."[110]

Since all organisms are composed of the same basic elements, take in nourishment from those same elements, live on the same planet, and are affected by the same physical laws, there is nothing unusual in their having a somewhat similar design. But there are also differences, differences that allow for some to operate in the air, others on land, and others in the water, and differences that their amazing DNA permits within basic kinds. These differences make up a wide gulf between them.

THE WIDEST GULF

Nowhere is the difference more pronounced than between man and any of the animals. There is a tremendous gulf that separates them, particularly with regard to mental ability.

Of all the living things on earth, man is the only one that can continue to improve upon his knowledge. Animals can learn a few things, but never progress beyond a certain point. Birds build nests, bees build hives, beavers build dams, but they never learn to improve these structures. There is not a single instance where an animal continues to build on accumulated knowledge. Only man has the ability.

Of the animals considered closest to man, the chimpanzee is said to be the most intelligent. But note what Dobzhansky says:

> "The chimpanzee is much superior to other nonhuman primates in memory, imagination, and learning ability. Nevertheless, there is a vast gulf between the intellectual capacity of chimpanzees and of man. Symbolic responses can be learned by chimpanzees only with considerable difficulty, and their frequency fails to increase with experience and age."[111]

All efforts to appreciably educate the chimpanzee, or any other member of the ape family, have failed. They soon exhaust their capacity to learn new things and cannot go beyond that. They remain what they are because their DNA allows for nothing more.

Does the evidence show a slow evolution for man's brain? In *Scientific American* of December 1953 anthropologist Loren C. Eiseley said that the arrival of the human brain, "measured in geologi-

A vast gulf separates man from the lower animals. It cannot be bridged, because they are different "kinds"

cal terms, appears to have been surprisingly sudden." He spoke of "this huge mushroom of a brain, which has arisen magically between night and morning," and added: "When I said that the human brain exploded, I meant no less."[112]

In the book *The Story of Man* evolutionist H. Mellersh said of man's brain: "His is a different brain, admittedly superior in no more than degree, yet in so great a degree as to constitute something virtually new in the world."[113]

This brain that "exploded" on the world scene is possessed by all races of mankind. The fact that primitive people today, such as the Australian aborigine, can be educated in one generation demonstrates what science knows to be true, that men everywhere, whether oriental, occidental, civilized or primitive have about the same high potential, a potential that creates a vast gulf between mankind and animal kind.

What helps to make man's brain superior is mentioned in *Life* magazine of June 28, 1963, where it says:

"Neurons in the brain make thousands of connections with each other. But the innumerable extra connections that the larger human cortex provides multiplies virtually to infinity the brain's capacity for receiving and analyzing data. And it is this sheer, massive power for handling data that places man in a class which is incomparably superior to any other living thing."[114]

The fantastic potential of the human brain was discussed by biochemist Isaac Asimov in the New York *Times Magazine* of October 9, 1966. He said: "Some estimates are that the brain, in a lifetime, absorbs as many as one million billion [1,000,000,000,000,000] separate bits of information. But there are some 10 billion gray cells, or neurons, in the brain." What potential does a single neuron hold? Asimov declares:

"A healthy, mature human being of normal intelligence may have upwards of 20 million RNA molecules [DNA's 'messenger'] in each neuron. . . . An RNA molecule made up of merely 25 links could have any one of a million billion different combinations, . . . In fact, every RNA molecule contains many hundreds of units—not merely 25. There is no question, then, that RNA presents a filing system perfectly capable of handling any load of learning and memory which the human being is likely to put upon it—and a billion times more than that quantity, too."[115]

Why would evolution provide something so fantastic as this and then not make full use of it for thousands of years, *not even today?* Such an astounding capacity for remembering, filing and using knowledge, a capacity far beyond what anyone could ever use in one lifetime of seventy years or more, would indicate that the human brain was designed by its Creator to last indefinitely, forever! Animals, on the other hand, have no such capabilities, but were designed for a much more limited sphere of activity as well as life-span.

That is just what the Bible shows. Man, with his marvelous brain, was created with a high degree of intellect. He was designed to live forever on earth and was given a brain that would serve that purpose. No animal was so designed.—Genesis 1: 27, 28; Psalm 37:29; John 17:3.

Yes, there is an unbridgeable gap between man and beast. If evolution were true, there should be no such gulf. There should be in-between stages of intelligence, but these are nowhere to be found. Evolutionists claim that these stages were the "prehistoric" men that are now extinct. But why should inferior animals such as the apes have survived and all the supposedly superior "pre-historic" men have disappeared? Indeed, did such "prehistoric" men ever exist?

CHAPTER 8

Are Apelike Men
Our Ancestors?

EVOLUTIONISTS maintain that there were "prehistoric" men, "apelike" men that filled the gap between man and animal, but that they are now extinct. Of these *Science News Letter* of May 29, 1965, said:

> "They [evolutionists] see our ancestors as hairy, tailless, and a little larger than present-day gibbons. They had mobile facial muscles and no 'mental eminence.' . . .
>
> "They were expert climbers and spent much of their lives in trees. On the ground they could stand with a semi-upright posture. They could walk on all fours and could run on their feet. . . .
>
> "The proto-hominoids apparently did not have the power of speech."[116]

From such descriptions drawings and plaster-cast figures of "prehistoric" men flood the literature and museums of the world. Brutish, beastly looking "ape-men" in a chain leading to modern man constantly confront the observer. But how much of this chain is built on solid fact? How much of it is built on sheer speculation?

Concerning this chain, evolutionist Rostand says:

> "We are still arguing, and doubtless will continue to argue for a long time, about the real connection among all these forms. . . . Did man

descend from an ape resembling the anthropoids we know today? Or from an inferior ape? Or even from a primate which did not as yet deserve the name of ape?"[117]

Why is there such difficulty? *New Scientist* of March 25, 1965, points out: "One of the prime difficulties is that really significant human fossil skulls are exceptionally rare: everything which has been found to date could be tucked away in a large coffin. All the rest must be referred to something else."[118]

The following comment in *Scientific American* of June 1956 also bears this out:

"Primatologists may therefore be forgiven their fumblings over great gaps of millions of years from which we do not possess a single complete monkey skeleton, let alone the skeleton of a human forerunner. . . . we have to read the story of primate evolution from a few handfulls of broken bones and teeth. Those fossils, moreover, are from places thousands of miles apart on the Old World land mass. . . .

"In the end we may shake our heads, baffled . . . It is as though we stood at the heart of a maze and no longer remembered how we had come there."[119]

An additional difficulty is noted in *Evolution as a Process*, edited by evolutionist Julian Huxley. We read:

"In the great majority of cases the descriptions of the specimens that have been provided by their discoverers have been so turned as to indicate that the fossils in question have some special place or significance in the line of direct human descent, as opposed to that of the family of apes. It is . . . unlikely that they could all enjoy this distinction . . .

"In the case of primate evolution the inferences are sometimes very insecurely based because of inadequacies of the evidence."[120]

However, evolutionists do generally agree now that man and the ape family branched off from a common ancestor. What is the fossil evidence for this common ancestor? *New Scientist* stated in 1965: "The unmistakable correspondence between man and anthropoids points clearly to a common ancestor. But it has not yet been found and we may have some difficulty in recognizing it."[121] So while evolutionists claim that man *must* have come from an apelike beast, the common ancestor of both man and ape, the evidence is simply not there! The conclusion is without supporting facts, as *The Saturday Evening Post* of December 3, 1966, verified: "Investigators . . . have yet to trace the origins of the human line."[122]

Is there any evidence of the early steps that supposedly came after this common ancestor? The evolutionary writers of the 1965 book *The Primates* admitted: "Unfortunately, the early stages of man's evolutionary progress along his individual line remain a total mystery."[123] And *Scientific American* of November 1966 said: "The nature of the line leading to living man . . . remains a matter of pure theory."[124]

Is the evidence more solid as we advance up the proposed chain? From a conference of prominent anthropologists that met in 1965 a timetable emerged. A diagram and an article based on this was published in the New York *Times* of April 11, 1965. It said: "Even today surprisingly little is known of man's own family tree. . . . there are still enormous gaps." However, it began the fossil evidence by saying: "At least 30 million years ago the features that distinguish man from all other animals had begun to emerge." The first specimen put in the chart was called Propliopithecus, a gibbon-like creature, fragments of which have been found in Egypt.

What was the next step listed? The *Times* reported: "A further step was the appearance, some 19 million years ago, of a genus with certain tooth features typical of man and the great apes." This was called Dryopithecus, found in Africa and Eurasia. So from Propliopithecus, about 30,000,-000 B.C.E., to Dryopithecus, about 19,000,000 B.C.E., there is a gigantic gap of about 11,000,000 years in which there is no evidence. The *Times* also said that after the disappearance of Dryopithecus "some nine million years ago, the record is blank for seven million years."[125]

What does all of this show so far? First of all, that the facts in support of the claim that there was a common ancestor of man and apes are missing. Then the supposed early record of untold millions of years in man's line is a total blank. Finally, from when the first evidence is said to have appeared, about 30,000,000 years ago until now, there are gaps amounting to about 18,000,000 years. Most of the chain from the assumed common ancestor to modern man is blank! There are no facts! It is little wonder that *Scientific American* stated in July 1964: "Pending additional discoveries it may be wiser not to insist that the transition from ape to man is now being documented from the fossil record."[126]

Yet, this fossil evidence just presented is even more feeble. How so? Because some evolutionists put Propliopithecus, not in man's line, but in a line leading to the gibbons; and they put Dryopithecus in another line that leads to the apes. They believe that the oldest creature in man's line is one called Ramapithecus. The *Times* said of this: "Midway through the lifetime of [Dryopithecus], about 12 million years ago, ape-like creatures with almost human faces appeared. This was the genus Ramapithecus, . . . found in the Siwalik Hills of northwest India."[127] Of course, this would mean an even larger gap from it back to that supposed common ancestor of man and ape.

Between Ramapithecus and the next ancestor listed up the chain, called Australopithecus, there is another huge gap. *Science News* of January 28, 1967, said: "Unfortunately, there is a 10 million-year gap in the fossil record between the latest Ramapithecus and the earliest of the Australopithecus."[128] Using the dates of these sources, the record from about 12,000,000 B.C.E. to about 2,000,000 is blank. Yet, what of Ramapithecus itself? *The Saturday Evening Post* stated:

> "It probably looked something like a small chimpanzee, and had the nimble hands and general agility of a monkey. . . .
> "The presumption is strong that Ramapithecus, the earliest known (but not the earliest) member of the family of man, was at least as ingenious as contemporary chimpanzees.
> "We have only a fleeting glimpse of Ramapithecus, the equivalent of a few frames clipped from a feature-length motion picture."[129]

From the description of Ramapithecus that evolutionists themselves give, it is evident to the unprejudiced that this is far, far more likely a species of animal in the ape or monkey family. The claim that it belongs in the line of man is pure speculation. Indeed, some evolutionists do not accept it as being in man's line. In the book *The Fossil Evidence for Human Evolution* the evolutionist author writes:

> "We can contrive a theoretical picture of the intermediate stages which presumably must have

been interposed between generalized pongid [ape] ancestors and the Australopithecus phase; but, in the absence of the concrete evidence of fossil remains, this is not a very satisfying procedure."[130]

It certainly is not satisfying to see a chain of ascent described from that assumed common ancestor to the Australopithecines with nothing to support it but speculation. But why should such theorizing be accepted without supporting facts?

THE AUSTRALOPITHECINES

What of the next stage, the Australopithecines? These are said to have appeared about 2,000,000 B.C.E. It is claimed that they were toolmakers, but it is admitted their brain was only about a third as large as modern man's.

Also, a similar fossil was found by Dr. L. Leakey in Africa several years ago. Of this the New York *Times* of April 11, 1965, said: "An apparent tooluser described by Dr. Leakey as Homo Habilis, is classed by Dr. Robinson and others as a form of Australopithecus."[131] Then, the book *The Primates* declared: "These finds provided the basis for the first coherent and satisfactory explanation of how man came to evolve out of his apelike ancestors."[132] It took a century of intensive hunting for a few bones that are regarded as "the first coherent and satisfactory explanation" of man's evolution from an apelike ancestor!

But is it all so certain that the Australopithecines were really apelike men? Evolutionist Le Gros Clark cautioned: "The terms 'man' and 'human' can only be applied to them with some reserve, for there is no certain evidence that they possessed any of the special attributes which are commonly associated with the human beings of today."[133]

What of their claimed toolmaking ability? *Science* of December 13, 1957, contained an article entitled "Australopithecines Contemporaneous with Man?" It stated:

> "J. T. Robinson reports the discovery of 58 stone artifacts . . . at Sterkfontein, Union of South Africa. This discovery is of great interest because this particular breccia also contains remains of Australopithecines, the early Pleistocene 'man-apes' of South Africa. . . .
>
> "Robinson concludes that the advanced character of this stone industry makes its attribution to the Australopithecines dubious; . . . He believes that the most reasonable hypothesis at the present time is to attribute the industry to a 'euhominid' (true man). . . .
>
> "Mason thinks that tool-making of the complexity shown in the Sterkfontein industry was probably beyond the ability of the Australopithecines and that it must be ascribed to some more advanced hominid."[134]

In *Science* of November 29, 1957, appeared the article "Hunters or Hunted?" It said:

> "During recent years, Raymond A. Dart, to whom belongs the credit of having discovered the first of the Australopithecines, has written at considerable length about the social life of these interesting and controversial 'man-apes' . . . Yet the data upon which his deductions are based, and hence his conclusions themselves, have proved somewhat short of convincing to at least some students of human evolution.
>
> "The evidence advanced by Dart for the deliberate use of fire by these creatures has not withstood critical analysis. Moreover, competent students, such as Oakley, have ascribed the accumulations of nonaustralopithecine bones found in the australopithecine deposits to the activities of carnivores, including hyenas. . . .
>
> "Washburn . . . concludes that it is 'probable that the australopithecines were themselves the game, rather than the hunters.' "[135]

For these and other reasons some evolutionists view these fossil remains as belonging to a terminal group of apes, and not ancestral to man at all. R. L. Lehrman, an evolutionist, said in his 1961 book *The Long Road to Man:* "Australopithecus was merely an upright, intelligent ape, not a man. The small braincase bearing heavy ridges over the eyes, across the back, and down the center was like that of any ape."[136] Also, Ashley Montagu in *Man: His First Million Years* stated in 1957: "The skull form of all australopithecines is extremely apelike. . . . Such creatures could not have been directly ancestral to man. . . . the australopithecines show too many specialized and apelike characters to be either the direct ancestors of man or of the line that led to man."[137]

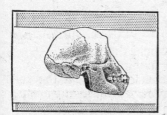

Extinct ape

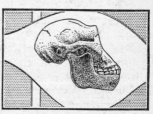

Australopithecinae

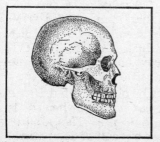

Modern man

Extinct form of ape and australopithecine model displayed in American Museum of Natural History, New York. Skull on left is modern man. Do australopithecines more closely resemble man or the ape? There is no evidence whatsoever that they are man's ancestors

MORE RECENT FOSSILS

The next significant step listed by evolutionists in the chain up to man includes many fossils previously listed separately and called by various names. These are now lumped together in the same genus as modern man, *Homo sapiens* [wise man], but in a different species, *Homo erectus* [erect man]. *World Book Encyclopedia* says:

> "*Homo erectus*, or erect man, is the name many scientists give to all fossil races with a human body and a brain ranging between 700 and 1,100 cc. *Homo erectus* ranks a step above Australopithecus and one below *Homo sapiens*, or modern man. Three varieties, or subspecies, have been clearly identified. The first, Java Man, . . . may be around 500,000 years old. The second, Peking Man, . . . dates from about 360,000 years ago. The third, Chellean Man, was found in Tanganyika, . . . about 400,000 years old."[138]

Is there complete agreement as to what these fossils are? No, for the *Encyclopedia Americana* states: "Some authorities held that they belonged to an ape, but a more manlike ape than any hitherto known; others considered them the remains of a lower type of man."[139] But in any event, as *Scientific American* of May 1965 points out: "Students of early man agree that modern *Homo sapiens* evolved directly from *Homo erectus*."

With such agreement that man evolved from *Homo erectus*, would it not seem that the evidence must be overwhelming? Just what is that evidence? *Scientific American* adds: "There is no direct evidence for the transition."[140]

How can any agreement be obtained that *Homo erectus* evolved into *Homo sapiens* when it is admitted that there is no evidence? This kind of agreement can come only as a result of dogmatism, blind faith, credulity, asserting to be true what one wants to be true. But certainly this is not a scientific procedure.

Notice too that *Scientific American* of November 1966 says a recent fossil find in Hungary "places a population of more progressive, *sapiens* humanity contemporary with the populations of *Homo erectus.*"[141] Also, in the 1964 book *Biology and Its Relation to Mankind* Professor of Biology A. M. Winchester says:

> "The remains of a Swanscombe man in Europe, the Kanjera man in Africa, and others suggest that true man may have existed as long as 300,000 years ago, which would have made him a contemporary of *Homo erectus.*"[142]

So *Homo erectus,* if human, was no more than a branch of mankind, possibly degenerate, that became extinct as did other races.

Then there are other fossils that were once considered much lower than modern-type man. But these are now known to be similar to modern man and are also classed as *Homo sapiens. World Book Encyclopedia* says in this regard:

> "Homo sapiens, or *wise man,* is the name usually given to all races with a human body and a brain measuring from 1,100 cc. upward, and averaging between 1,350 and 1,500 cc. This group includes all modern men. *Pre-Neanderthals* are the earliest examples of *Homo sapiens.* They date from about 300,000 B.C. Archaeologists have found skull fragments near Swanscombe, England, and Steinheim, Germany."[143]

Neanderthal men were once believed to be "ape-men," missing links, the direct ancestors of modern man. But *Harper's* magazine of December 1962 reported: "The Neanderthals were not stunted, bent over, nor brutal as commonly claimed. Many of them did, however, suffer from arthritis."[144] And the *Times Magazine* of March 19,

1961, even gave the brain capacity of Neanderthal man as 1,625 c.c., larger than that of the average modern man.[145] Interesting, too, is the following description of them that *World Book Encyclopedia* of 1966 gives:

> "At first, scientists thought that Neanderthal Man was a squat, stooping, brutish, somewhat apelike creature. But later research showed that the bodies of Neanderthal men and women were completely human, fully erect, and very muscular. Their brains were as large as those of modern man."[146]

While admitting such to be the case, this same *World Book Encyclopedia* of 1966, under a different heading,[147] has a picture of a Neanderthal family, depicting them as 'squat, stooping, brutish and somewhat apelike'! This is no exception, for most books, drawings and museum exhibits still present Neanderthal man as being stooped over

A modern encyclopedia says Neanderthal men were not "squat, stooping, brutish, somewhat apelike," but were "completely human, fully erect." Yet, under another heading it shows the above exhibit from the Chicago Natural History Museum portraying them as "squat, stooping, brutish, somewhat apelike," including the child!

and moronic looking, giving the impression that here is an apelike ancestor of man.

Other fossils that also were once placed in different categories are now classed the same as modern man. Those known as Cro-Magnons resembled modern man in all important aspects. In fact, *Science Digest* said: "Since the Cro-Magnon man . . . the human brain has been decreasing in size."[148] This indicates degeneration, not evolution. Similarly the Chicago *Tribune,* commenting on the remarks of Dr. Ernst Mayr about the human brain, says: "The trend, now, may be in a downward direction. . . . The Harvard scientist says the increase in human brain size—a characteristic that sets man apart from all other animals—stopped nearly 100,000 years ago."[149]

That many of the fossils once listed as "prehistoric" are not such at all is seen from the striking fact that fossils of modern-type men have been found in the same strata, or even in earlier ones than "prehistoric" fossils. Most evolutionists choose to ignore these, for they do not fit the preconceived idea of transformation from the brute beast. *Biology and Its Relation to Mankind* comments:

> "There was a time when it was thought that perhaps modern man was a direct descendant of the Java man, the Rhodesian man, and the Neanderthal man. As the evidence has accumulated, however, it appears that this is not possible, because some ancient remains of true man have been found which were contemporary with the remains of some of these other forms."[150]

This same point was noted in 1963 by Professor F. Marsh, a biologist, in *Evolution or Special Creation?* He said:

> "Another example of tampering with the evidence was furnished by Dubois, who admitted,

many years after his sensational report of finding the remains of Java Man, . . . that he had found at the same time in the same deposits bones that were unquestionably those of modern humans."[151]

In this same regard *The Bible and Modern Science* states:

"It is of great significance that many fossilized skeletons of modern man have been found at many different locations, and often with every indication of being as old as or older than the supposedly less advanced hominoids that have been unearthed. . . .

"There is no real evidence against the far more reasonable theory, adopted by some, that the Neanderthals, Peking Man, etc., represent degenerate races, descended from Homo sapiens as a result of mutation, isolation, etc. In fact, there is some evidence that modern man himself is a somewhat deteriorated descendant of the ancestors. The Cro-Magnon race of men, who inhabited Europe about the same time as the Neanderthals, are well known to have been superior to modern man, both in physical size and in brain capacity."[152]

DECEPTION

If many fossils were merely varieties of *Homo sapiens,* how can we account for their beastlike appearance? Certainly in many drawings and in museum displays they have an apish look.

But are such drawings and figures of apelike men scientific? Can it be determined what a fossil really looked like, that is, what its facial features were, the skin, hair and coloring? In this connection evolutionist Le Gros Clark in *The Fossil Evidence for Human Evolution* observes:

"Now it is probable that there are no racial types in which the skull characters are more distinctive than Negroes and Eskimos; and yet experts fail to agree when faced with single

Zinjanthropus
as drawn for
"Sunday Times,"
April 5, 1964

Zinjanthropus
as drawn for
prominent scientist

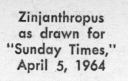

Zinjanthropus
as drawn for
"National Geographic,"
September 1960

Three different interpretations of what the fossil Zinjanthropus looked like. This demonstrates "the impossibility of reconstructing hair, eyes, nose, lips or facial expression"

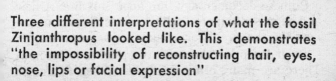

skulls whose claims to these types are in question. If a decision proves so difficult in such cases, it will be realized how much more difficult, or even impossible, it will be to identify, by reference to limited skeletal remains, minor racial groups with less distinctive characters."[153]

Corroborating this, Ivar Lissner in *Man, God and Magic* says:

"Just as we are slowly learning that primitive men are not necessarily savages, so we must learn to realize that the early men of the Ice Age were neither brute beasts nor semi-apes nor cretins. Hence the ineffable stupidity of all attempts to reconstruct Neanderthal or even Peking man. Exaggeratedly hirsute plaster figures of bestial mien glower savagely at us in museums all over the world, their features usually chocolate-brown in color, their hair wild and unkempt, their jaws prognathous and their foreheads receding—and this despite the fact that we have absolutely no idea what color Paleolithic man's skin was or how his hair grew and virtually no idea of his physiognomy. The American authority T. D. Stewart rightly pointed out in 1948 the impossibility of reconstructing hair, eyes, nose, lips or facial expression. 'The probabilities are that the expression of early man was not less benign than our own,' he wrote."[154]

So, contrary to what true scientific facts would allow, evolutionists have given fossils the appearance that suited their preconceived theories. That is why it is possible to read information such as the following that appeared in the New York *Times* in 1959: "The Peking man, a 500,000-year-old fossil, has had his face redone for a starring role in a Chinese documentary film about his life. A new and supposedly more lifelike reconstruction of the head of the prehistoric human was reported."[155]

Such deceptive alteration of evidence is not new. There are many other examples. When Professor

Dubois, the Dutch surgeon, discovered Java Man in 1891-92, where did he find the fossil remains? The *Encyclopædia Britannica* tells us:

> "The five fossil fragments found were: a skull cap which outwardly had the form which might be expected in a giant form of gibbon, a left thigh bone and three teeth. The most distant parts of the fragments were 20 paces apart. Later he added a sixth fragment—part of a lower jaw found in another part of the island but in a stratum of the same geological age."[156]

How scientific is it to collect scraps of bones, twenty yards or so apart, add to them another scrap found miles away, and claim that they all belonged together?

Another example is given by evolutionist Le Gros Clark:

> "There is a danger of relying on too few measurements, . . . An example of this difficulty is provided by the famous case of Hesperopithecus. This generic name was given to a fossil tooth found in Nebraska in 1922, on the assumption that it represented an extinct type of anthropoid ape. . . . As is well known, the tooth proved later to be that of a fossil peccary [a piglike animal]. . . . there can be few paleontologists who have not erred in this way at some time or another!"[157]

Of another discovery the *Encyclopædia Britannica,* in its 1946 edition, said:

> "The discovery which ranks next in importance . . . was made by Mr. Charles Dawson at Piltdown, Sussex, between the years 1911 and 1915. He found the greater part of the left half of a deeply mineralized human skull, also part of the right half; the right half of the lower jaw, damaged at certain parts but carrying the first and second molar teeth and the socket of the third molar or wisdom tooth. . . .

"Amongst British authorities there is now agreement that the skull and the jaw are parts of the same individual."[158]

No doubt the reader familiar with evolutionary matters will recognize the above as the "Piltdown Man." How "scientific" was this "agreement" among British "authorities"? *Science News Letter* of February 25, 1961, reminds us:

"One of the most famous fakes exposed by scientific proof was Piltdown man, found in Sussex, England, . . . and thought by some to be 500,000 years old. After much controversy, it turned out to be not a primitive man at all but a composite of a skull of modern man and the jawbone of an ape. . . . The jawbone had been 'doctored' with bichromate of potash and iron to make it look mineralized."[159]

In addition to staining the skull, the teeth had been filed down to make them appear worn. As the *Reader's Digest* of October 1956 wrote: "Every important piece proved a forgery. Piltdown Man was a fraud from start to finish! . . . all the circumstantial evidence points to Dawson as the author of the hoax."[160]

The extent to which some evolutionists have stooped to manufacture the facts that are so glaringly missing for their theory is also revealed in the January 1965 *Scientific American*. It tells of a meteorite that contained organic material and was used to support evolution:

"A fragment of a meteorite that fell in southwest France more than a century ago has proved on recent inspection to be ingeniously doctored with terrestrial organic material. . . .
"The hoaxer had apparently moistened the meteorite fragment until it was soft, inserted the various foreign bodies and then, using glue as a binder, faked a surface crust of the kind produced

by atmospheric heating to replace the one destroyed by his manipulations. . . .

"The Orgueil fall had occurred only five weeks after Pasteur had delivered his stormy and widely reported defense of divine creation as the only possible initiator of life."[161]

Also deceptive is the way evolutionary matters are often presented to the unwary. Time and again fossils are lined up to make the casual observer conclude that they came from one another, but on further investigation it is found that this is not even generally accepted among evolutionists. Another example is the suggestion that man evolved from an ape. Although evolutionary theory no longer makes that claim, but rejects it, we find such wording as the chapter heading in the 1965 book *The Primates,* which says: "From Ape toward Man."[162]

Truly, the fossil evidence and corresponding reconstructions presented for man's evolution is the shabbiest excuse for "science." It is built on fantastic assertions and speculations, with the evolutionary chain shredded by gigantic gaps in time, place and shape.

The true scientific facts point, not to the evolution of man from the beasts, but to the creation of man as a kind separate and distinct from the animals. He remains as such to this day. He cannot cross with any of the animals because his DNA does not allow for it. He remains within his Genesis kind, has always done so, and will always do so.

VESTIGIAL ORGANS

Evolutionists point to what they call "vestigial" organs in man as constituting proof for human evolution. These are said to be the last vestiges of organs that once had a use, but are now no longer needed because of the advance up the evolutionary ladder. But note what an article in the November 1966 *Reader's Digest*, entitled "The 'Useless' Gland That Guards Our Health," states:

> "For at least 2000 years, doctors have puzzled over the function of a pinkish-gray bit of tissue lying just below the neck and behind the breast-bone—the thymus gland. . . . Modern physicians came to regard it, like the appendix, as a useless, vestigial organ which had lost its original purpose, if indeed it ever had one.
>
> "In the last few years, however, the dogged detective work of a small band of Americans, Britons, Australians and Swedes has cracked the thymus enigma. These men have proved that, far from being useless, the thymus is really the master gland that regulates the intricate immunity system which protects us against infectious diseases. . . .
>
> "But is the thymus the only organ regulating our immunity system? Recent experiments have led researchers to believe that the appendix, tonsils and adenoids may also figure in the antibody responses."[163]

The *Encyclopædia Britannica* also said in this regard: "Many of the so-called vestigial organs are now known to fulfill important functions."[164]

The ignorance of the function of a particular organ is no reason to call it vestigial. Nor is its malfunctioning proof that it is vestigial. There are probably more cases of throat ailments each year than there are of appendicitis, but no one would call the throat a "vestigial" organ. Besides, evolution must show the evolving of new organs, more useful ones. Any organ that is indeed degenerating is hardly a proof for evolution, but is rather a support for the degeneracy of man, a downward movement instead of an upward one.

CHAPTER 9

How Old Is Man?

A FUNDAMENTAL part of the evolution theory is that life evolved slowly over hundreds of millions of years. Does this not disprove the Bible's teaching that man has been on earth only about 6,000 years and that the earth and all life upon it were created within six "days"?

The Bible gives no specific time period to the actual creating of the earth. Of the material universe, including the earth, the simple Bible statement is: "In the beginning God created the heavens and the earth." (Genesis 1:1) This allows for thousands of millions of years that the material of the earth could have been in existence before being inhabited by living things.

After this the Bible tells of six "days" during which life appeared. But the Bible's use of the word "day" here means a period of time and not a twenty-four-hour day. Genesis 2:4 indicates this by speaking of the "day that Jehovah God made earth and heaven," when previously it called each one of six periods included in that same time a "day." Because of the way it is used in the Bible, the word "day" often means simply a period of time, and cannot be confined to meaning just twenty-four hours. This can be verified by checking the word in an exhaustive Bible concordance and noting its many usages.

But what about the great time difference between the Bible's nearly 6,000 years for man's existence and the millions of years claimed for it by evolutionists? Let us examine the dating methods evolutionists use and see how accurate they are.

One method of dating determines the amount of radioactive carbon (C-14) left in bones, wood, charcoal, or some other once-living object. C-14 is an unstable element that decays. It is also called radiocarbon and is formed by the activity of cosmic rays on the earth's atmosphere. Plants absorb C-14 from the atmosphere. When man (or an animal) eats the plants, his body absorbs the C-14 from the plant. At death, this accumulating of C-14 in the body stops, and what is already present continues to decay and is not replaced. In about 5,600 years the C-14 is thought to be half gone, so it is said to have a half-life of that time.

Thus, scientists take bone, wood, charcoal or other once-living objects and get an idea of their age by measuring the C-14 left. If it is half gone, the object is considered about 5,600 years old. If it is three-quarters gone, it is considered twice that old, and so on. The method is limited because of its short half-life, so items over about 50,000 years old cannot be dated by it.

What has this C-14 dating method revealed when tested on supposedly very old specimens connected with man? The vast majority of such samples showed that the radioactivity was above the halfway point, well within the 6,000-year span allowed for man's existence by the Bible. However, some objects that were dated have indicated man's existence to be somewhat longer than 6,000 years. Do not these estimates prove the time indicated by the Bible wrong?

First of all, it is vital to note that C-14 dating

is based on several assumptions, a most important one being mentioned at a recent conference of radiocarbon experts. *Science* magazine of December 10, 1965, tells about it:

> "Throughout the conference emphasis was placed on the fact that laboratories do not measure ages, they measure sample activities. The connection between activity and age is made through a set of assumptions. . . . one of the main assumptions of C-14 dating is that the atmospheric radiocarbon level has held steady over the age-range to which the method applies."[165]

What would happen if the C-14 level in the atmosphere has not remained steady? *Science Digest* of December 1960 said:

> "It most certainly would ruin some of our carefully developed methods of dating things from the past. . . .
>
> "If the level of carbon-14 was less in the past, due to a greater magnetic shielding from cosmic rays, then our estimates of the time that has elapsed since the life of the organism will be too long."[166]

Now, then, has the level of radiocarbon remained steady in the past? *Science Year* of 1966 reported: "Scientists have found that the C-14 concentration in the air and in the sea has not remained constant over the years, as originally supposed."[167]

What is often ignored, too, is the fact that there was a much greater shielding of the atmosphere from cosmic rays about 4,300 years ago. The Bible explains that prior to that time a vast water canopy was suspended high above the earth, and that its fall caused a global deluge in the days of the man Noah, who wrote an eyewitness account of the event. (Psalm 104:6, 7; Genesis 1:6, 7;

7:11, 12) This water canopy shielded the atmosphere from cosmic rays to a greater extent than is true today, thus reducing the formation of radiocarbon. That is why objects dated from before that time appear older than they really are, for they did not absorb as much C-14 as objects have absorbed since then.

Science magazine of December 11, 1959, commented about "the failure of the radiocarbon (C-14) technique to yield dates of certain dependability," and said:

> "Although it was hailed as the answer to the prehistorian's prayer when it was first announced, there has been increasing disillusion with the method because of the chronological uncertainties (in some cases, absurdities) that would follow a strict adherence to published C-14 dates. . . .
>
> "What bids to become a classic example of 'C-14 irresponsibility' is the 6000-year spread of 11 determinations for Jarmo, a prehistoric village in northeastern Iraq, which, on the basis of all archeological evidence, was not occupied for more than 500 consecutive years."[168]

That errors of thousands of years occur in the C-14 method was verified by *Science* of August 16, 1963, when it stated: "Errors of shell radiocarbon dates may be as large as several thousand years."[169]

It is therefore obvious that any radiocarbon dates that might indicate man to be more than 6,000 years old are no basis for discrediting the Bible's chronology for man.

However, have not some bones been given an age of several millions of years? What of the recent fossil find, a small part of an elbow bone, about which the front page of the New York *Times* of January 14, 1967, declared: "Bone Found in

Kenya Indicates Man Is 2.5 Million Years Old"?[170] How are such fossils dated?

The dating method used in these cases is not C-14, but is potassium-argon. *Scientific American* of September 1961 explains: "There is no way to date bone more than 50,000 years old, so they analyzed samples of rock from immediately above and below the level where the bones were found."[171] By measuring the content of potassium-40 and its decayed product, argon-40, scientists try to determine the age of the rock, particularly volcanic rock. If the age of the rock above is determined, then the bones underneath that rock must be as old or older.

However, the potassium-argon method is very uncertain in measuring the age of relatively recent volcanic rock. Why? Because radioactive potassium has a half-life of 1,300,000,000 years. In that vast time half of the potassium decays to become the gas argon. So measuring rocks just a few million years old is like trying to measure seconds on a clock that has only an hour hand. As *Natural History* of February 1967 noted: "The [potassium-argon] dating method is increasingly inaccurate for dates of less than one million years. Consequently, there is a period during Early and Middle Pleistocene times when dating human remains is difficult and uncertain."[172]

Also, potassium-argon dating of volcanic rock is made on a very weak assumption, the assumption being that the volcanic activity dispelled all the argon originally in the molten lava. But if only a trace of argon remained, the clock would not be set at zero, and ages measured by it would be far too high. In regard to a find of Leakey's from Olduvai Gorge in Africa, *Science* of April 2, 1965, observed: "The age of 1.75 million years . . . has been questioned . . . on the basis of the possibility of the material being defective—for example, the material may have contained radiogenic argon at the time of crystallization or may have suffered atmospheric contamination."[173] And scientists at Johns Hopkins University had said: "The dates are of doubtful value."[174] In addition, it has been found that the potassium-argon ages do not always fall in proper sequence; in some cases the bed lying underneath gave an age younger than the bed lying above it.

The potassium in the earth has been generating argon all the time. When rock is melted in volcanic activity, every bit of argon must have been boiled out for any reliable dating. But even if a minute trace remains, it could cause errors amounting to millions of years. It would take only the tiniest trace of argon inherited from the melted rock to make a 5,000-year-old bed of volcanic rock look 1,750,000 or 2,500,000 years old.

That the potassium-argon method is unreliable is shown by the following item in *Science Digest* of December 1962:

"Through radioactive dating methods [potassium-argon], the age of the earth has been approximated at 4,500 million years. A new and higher figure—6,500 million years—has now been given."[175]

Why this difference of 2,000,000,000 years? The article explains that the "new age for the earth may be the result of some overlooked factor in the potassium-argon dating technique."

There are other dating methods too, but none in any way disprove the 6,000-year age of mankind given by the Bible. True, animal fossils are older, but the Bible, in its account of creation in Genesis, allows for that. It shows that animals were created thousands of years before man.

But how can we account for the fact that many fossils are found buried under deep layers of earth and rock? Surely not all of this is the result of volcanic activity, is it?

CATASTROPHIC CHANGES

Evolutionists assumed that the earth's crust had not changed appreciably since living things appeared. Hence, when observing a fossil buried under many feet of earth and rock where no evidence of volcanic activity existed, they assumed it must be very old.

But the earth's crust has not remained undisturbed. Gigantic upheavals have buried fossils far beneath terrestrial matter that was much older than the fossils it covered. Of this type of upheaval *Newsweek* of December 23, 1963, said:

> "Catastrophism is a fighting word among geologists. It is a theory based on divine intervention, and its adherents held that the history of the earth and the life on it were moved by a series of disasters inspired by God—the last one Noah's Flood. It was the major line of thought for a few decades last century, but a vigorous counterattack by the naturalists against the supernaturalists eventually pushed it aside.

> "But now many geologists believe the counterattack may have been all too vigorous. In their haste to reject the hand of God, they have passed over some solid evidence that could help improve their understanding of geology and evolution. . . .

> "There is evidence, for example, that great expanses have been inundated within a matter of days. Such catastrophes were often followed by explosive development of different forms of life."

One paleontologist from the American Museum of Natural History added this comment:

"Geology students are taught that the 'present is the key to the past,' and they too often take it to mean that nothing ever happened that isn't happening now. But since the end of World War II, when a new generation moved in, we have gathered more data and we have begun to realize that there were many catastrophic events in the past, some of which happened just once."[176]

Science Year of 1965 also took note of drastic changes that have occurred in the earth's crust. It said: "The discovery of coal and fossil ferns in the Transantarctic Mountains, . . . was evidence of a warm climate in the past. Obviously, there had been a reversal of climate." And the caption under a picture of a geologist says he "stands atop unusual butte in Victoria Land. He believes formation is a result of a mammoth flood thousands of years ago."[177]

Gigantic torrents of water and earth movements have caused vast changes in the earth's

Gigantic torrents of water and huge earth movements buried many forms of life, some being frozen in icy, mucky graves and preserved for thousands of years

surface and climate, burying many forms of animals, and even man, under tons of earth. That is why we cannot just observe what is going on at present and necessarily use that as a measuring stick for what went on in the past.

That a flood, a catastrophe of immense proportions, did actually occur in the not-too-distant past is verified by the great number of fossils and carcasses deposited in icy, mucky dumps. This was noted in *The Saturday Evening Post* of January 16, 1960, which contained an article entitled "Riddle of the Frozen Giants." It said:

"About one seventh of the entire land surface of our earth, stretching in a great swath round the Arctic Ocean, is permanently frozen. . . . the greater part of it is covered with a layer, varying in thickness from a few feet to more than 1000 feet, of stuff we call muck. This is composed of an assortment of different substances, all bound together with frozen water, which becomes and acts as a rock. . . . it is usually for the most part composed of fine sand or coarse silt, but it also includes a high proportion of earth or loam, and often also masses of bones or even whole animals in various stages of preservation or decomposition. . . .

"The list of animals that have been thawed out of this mess would cover several pages. . . . The greatest riddle, however, is when, why and how did all these assorted creatures, and in such absolutely countless numbers, get killed, mashed up and frozen into this horrific indecency? . . .

"These animal remains were not in deltas, swamps or estuaries, but were scattered all over the country. . . . But last, and worst of all, many of these animals were perfectly fresh, whole and undamaged, and still either standing or at least kneeling upright. . . .

"Here is a really shocking—to our previous way of thinking—picture. Vast herds of enormous, well-fed beasts not specifically designed for extreme cold, placidly feeding in sunny pastures, delicately plucking flowering buttercups at a temperature in which we would probably not even have needed a coat. Suddenly they were all killed without any visible sign of violence and before they could so much as swallow a last mouthful of food, and then were quick-frozen so rapidly that every cell of their bodies is perfectly preserved."[178]

This is exactly what happened in the Flood the Bible speaks of. A gigantic downpour of water that undoubtedly was accompanied by freezing winds in polar regions engulfed living things when the water canopy surrounding the earth descended. (Genesis 7:11, 12) At the poles the temperature change would be the most rapid and drastic. The forms of life engulfed there would be preserved in the frozen muck. Toward the equator freezing would be less likely, but organisms would be covered with layers of silt and

This mammoth, uncovered by excavators in Siberia, was frozen solid in sitting position thousands of years ago by engulfing icy muck. Vegetation was still in its mouth and stomach. Its flesh was edible when thawed out

earth that would be much, much older than the buried creatures.

Such a cataclysm is discussed in the article "The Earth's Shifting Crust," by professor of history and anthropology C. H. Hapgood in *The Saturday Evening Post* of January 10, 1959. He says:

> "One of these periods of wholesale destruction of life occurred at the end of the last ice age. . . . It was a natural disaster which, according to one writer, destroyed some 40,000,000 animals in North America alone. . . . In a few thousand years life on earth assumed a radically new aspect. . . . It is apparent that millions of animals once flourished in areas now bitterly cold. . . .
>
> "With regard to the last ice age, we have recently come into possession of new information that deepens its mystery. . . . By use of the [radiocarbon] method, scientists revised the date of the end of the last ice age, making it only 10,000 years ago, instead of 30,000 years. . . .
>
> "This discovery challenged the fundamental principle of the system established by the nineteenth-century geologist, Charles Lyell. He supposed that geological processes in the past always proceeded at their present rates: processes such as rainfall, snowfall, erosion and the deposition of sediment. . . . there was a very marked acceleration of the rate of these geological processes during the last part of the ice age. Some factor must, therefore, have been operating that is not operating now. . . .
>
> "The other new method of dating, which we call the ionium method, has also produced a major upset. Applied to date the sediments obtained in cores from the bottom of the Ross Sea in Antarctica, it has revealed that during the last million years Antarctica has several times been nonglacial. When these cores were dated it was found that the most recent 'ice age' in the Ross Sea began only 6,000 years ago!"[179]

So science is discovering the facts, the truth of what the Bible shows, that there were catastrophes that caused great climatic and terrestrial changes. One such, the global deluge over 4,000 years ago, destroyed living things in vast numbers and covered them with layers of icy muck, sand, silt and earth.

THE EARLIEST RECORDS

It is commonly assumed that, when evolutionists talk about man as being on earth for hundreds of thousands of years, and reject the shorter period that the Bible gives, they have evidence to prove it. Even Nobel Prize-winning nuclear physicist W. F. Libby, a pioneer in radiocarbon dating, assumed this. Note what he says in the March 3, 1961, issue of *Science:*

> "The research in the development of the dating technique consisted of two stages—dating of samples from the historic and the prehistoric epochs, respectively. Arnold [a co-worker] and I had our first shock when our advisers informed us that history extended back only for 5,000 years. . . . You read statements to the effect that such and such a society or archeological site is 20,000 years old. We learned rather abruptly that these numbers, these ancient ages, are not known accurately; in fact, the earliest historical date that has been established with any degree of certainty is about the time of the 1st Dynasty in Egypt."[180]

The fact that man's records go back no farther than what the Bible allows, about 6,000 years, is repeatedly acknowledged. *The World Book Encyclopedia* says: "The earliest records we have of human history go back only about 5,000 years."[181] The *Encyclopedia Americana* says: "Social evolution in man, however, has occupied not more than 10,000 years. Most of it has happened in the last 6,000 years."[182] *Biology for Today* states concerning the age of metals: "This era began about 5000 years ago and extends to our present day."[183] *Re-*

Cuneiform letter with front of envelope broken away. No writing antedates the age of man given in the Bible

view *Text in Biology* declares: "The invention of writing, about 6000 years ago, ushered in the historic period of man. The time prior to 6000 years ago is known as the prehistoric period."[184] In *Man: His First Million Years* we read: "The earliest written language, Sumerian cuneiform, goes back to about 3500 B.C."[185]

These are what men offer as facts. But note how evolutionists add to these facts their speculations: In *Biology and Its Relation to Mankind*, 1964, by A. M. Winchester: "It is a common error to think of man's existence in terms of recorded history. Historical records go back to about 3,000 B.C., but this is only a small fraction of the time man has lived on earth."[186] In *Man: His First Million Years*, 1957, by A. Montagu: "Recorded history is no more than six thousand years old, whereas human beings have been making history ever since they have been on this earth, a period believed to be about one million years."[187] In *Biology and Human Progress*, 1958, by L. Eisman and C. Tanzer: "In the last six thousand years, man has advanced far more rapidly than he did in the million or more years of his prehistoric existence."[188]

It is well to note why the last 6,000 years is called the "historic" period of man. In this period it has been proved that man existed. Science has the facts, the records, documents, cities, monuments, writings and other artifacts to verify it. But before that period man did not leave such evidence of his existence. That is why it is called "prehistoric." But the entire idea of a "prehistoric" period for man is based solely on assumption, speculation. It is pure theory, devised to support another theory, evolution.

That man is a relative newcomer, but was equipped for rapid development, can be seen from such findings as that noted in *New Discoveries in Babylonia About Genesis*. The author, P. J. Wiseman, says:

> "No more surprising fact has been discovered by recent excavation, than the suddenness with which civilization appeared in the world. This discovery is the very opposite to that anticipated. It was expected that the more ancient the period, the more primitive would excavators find it to be, until traces of civilization ceased altogether and aboriginal man appeared. Neither in Babylonia nor Egypt, the lands of the oldest known habitations of man, has this been the case."[189]

But is not the generation-by-generation increase in knowledge that has been characteristic of the historic period proof of evolution? No, not if by "evolution" we mean the changing of one kind of life into another kind. The ancient Babylonians, Egyptians and Greeks thousands of years ago were as natively intelligent as our generation. What they lacked was the vast storehouse of accumulated knowledge to draw on that we have today. Building on the knowledge of others is not organic evolution. It is simply progress, the ability to do so being created within man from the beginning.

In *Science World* of February 1, 1961, this matter is commented on in this way:

> "Contrary to popular belief, man has long since ceased to evolve. Present day man, the human being that we are, does not differ essentially from the human being who lived 100,000 years ago.
>
> "The whole of that part of man's history which has gone by since those far-away ages has not, or has scarcely, altered our species. The enormous difference which nonetheless exists between the ancient flint-chipper and his modern heir is entirely the work of civilization—of the culture accumulated and transmitted by social tradition.
>
> "If, by some miracle, it were possible to fetch a new-born child of that past age into our own time, and to bring him up as one of ours, he would become a man exactly like us."[190]

The Encyclopedia Americana states in this regard: "Most of what is popularly regarded as evolution of man is social, not biological, evolution. . . . Almost none of the human social evolution has been biological evolution."[191]

That the ancients already had a high brain capacity is demonstrated by this item in the New York *Times* about a discovery in Iraq:

> "Schoolboys of the little Sumerian county seat of Shadippur about 2000 B.C. had a 'textbook' with the solution of Euclid's classic triangle problem seventeen centuries before Euclid . . .
>
> "Clay 'textbooks' of the schoolboys of Shadippur contain an encyclopedic outline of the scientific knowledge of their time, which will necessitate a sharp revision of the history of the development of science and, accordingly, of the story of the development of the human mind. . . .
>
> "It suggests that mathematics reached a stage of development about 2000 B.C. that archaeologists and historians of science had never imagined possible."[192]

This harmonizes completely with the Bible account. It also helps to explain why an aborigine today, almost in a "prehistoric" condition, can be educated within one generation to take his place in our complicated human society. His brain is not inferior, but his accumulated knowledge is. When he is exposed to proper education, he advances much like any other human. It has always been so from man's creation nearly 6,000 years ago.

DEGENERATION

As man, with his high brain capacity, spread out over the earth, he developed separate cultures, some more advanced than others. This was due, not to evolution, but to geography and changed languages. (Genesis 11:8, 9) The fact that some of the cultures degenerated into a "stone age," as we can see today in New Guinea, Africa or among the Australian aborigines, simply demonstrates that man's progress was not automatic, but could be reversed. Particularly is this so when we consider that the Bible states that man was created with a perfect mind and body but, because of rebellion against God, has been degenerating.—Genesis 3: 19; Romans 5:12.

That "primitive" men today are not in an earlier stage of evolution, science is beginning to recognize. *Science Year* of 1966, reporting on a conference of anthropologists, said:

"Many of the so-called 'primitive' peoples of the world today, most of the participants agreed, may not be so primitive after all. They suggested that certain hunting tribes in Africa, Central India, South America, and the Western Pacific are not relics of the Stone Age, as had been previously thought, but instead are the 'wreckage' of more highly developed societies forced through various circumstances to lead a much simpler, less-developed life."[193]

All races descended from the first man and woman. Some developed more highly than others, building on accumulated knowledge. Some progressed for a time, then retrogressed. Others eventually became extinct

The same observation is noted in connection with languages. Man's degeneration from perfection, as described in the Bible, should be shown in his languages. In the September 3, 1955, *Science News Letter* the following comments regarding this point appear:

> "There are no primitive languages, declares Dr. Mason, who is a specialist on American languages. The idea that 'savages' speak in a series of grunts, and are unable to express many 'civilized' concepts, is very wrong. . . .
>
> " 'In fact, many of the languages of non-literate peoples are far more complex than modern European ones,' Dr. Mason said. . . .
>
> "Evolution in language, Dr. Mason has found, is just the opposite of biological evolution. Languages have evolved from the complex to the simple."[194]

The same thought is expressed by evolutionist Ashley Montagu in his book *Man: His First Million Years:*

> "Many 'primitive' languages . . . are often a great deal more complex and more efficient than the languages of the so-called higher civilizations."[195]

From such facts we must conclude that any so-called "prehistoric" men, if they were *Homo sapiens* at all, were simply offshoots of humankind who lived contemporaneously with men who were like us today. These branches became separated, ethnically and geographically, from the main streams of humanity. They made little or no progress, or actually retrogressed and eventually died out. Of this the *Encyclopædia Britannica* of 1966 says:

> "In the early days of paleoanthropological discovery, *H. neanderthalensis* was commonly

assumed to represent the ancestral type from which *H. sapiens* derived ... But the accumulation of further discoveries made it clear that these apparently primitive features are secondary—the result of a retrogressive evolution from still earlier types which do not appear to be specifically distinguishable from *H. sapiens*. . . . Thus, the specialized Neanderthal type of *Homo* seems to have been preceded by a more generalized type. The brain of the specialized type was, surprisingly, rather large, for the mean cranial capacity actually exceeded that of modern human races."[196]

That the degenerative effects of Adam's rebellion upon all his descendants cannot be eliminated by man is becoming more clear. In the New York *Times* of October 30, 1966, the article, "Medicine: The Mystery of Why We Grow Old," states:

"At the moment, efforts to lengthen the life span seem to have broken down. . . . it is now generally agreed that no single factor is involved in aging. . . . the conquest of cancer, heart disease and the like will not lead to a dramatic increase in the life span. Too many weaknesses are built into the human frame to be overcome."[197]

Evolutionist Rostand similarly stated: "If we take into account only the facts of hereditary variation which occurred in mankind, it seems that mankind must fear decadence rather than anticipate progress."[198]

All the facts that science has uncovered verify the Bible's account of man's degeneration. The Bible record states that man was created perfect but, because of rebelling against his Maker, began degenerating. His sin caused a 6,000-year-long decline morally and physically. The depths to which man has sunk are evident from the morally depraved condition of society today. And it is not improving, but is getting worse.

CHAPTER 10

Living Testimony
to a Creator

Y ET, even in man's imperfect state, his complex physical makup is living testimony to a superior Designer or Maker. The psalmist David long ago was moved to say of his Maker: "I shall laud you because in a fear-inspiring way I am wonderfully made. Your works are wonderful, as my soul is very well aware."—Psalm 139:14.

Cause for astonishment at the body's remarkable functions has not diminished since David's time. Indeed, despite human imperfection, the more man learns, the greater becomes his reason for awe and admiration at how the body is designed. In 1966, Dr. W. W. Akers, a Rice University engineer working with surgeons to build an artificial heart, exclaimed: "The body is the ultimate in technological perfection. Almost any machine you can dream up—no matter how sophisticated—you can look into the body and find one better."[199] What is especially amazing is the formation of a baby within its mother's womb.

At one time you were a single fertilized egg, one cell smaller than the period at the end of this sentence. From that simple, minute beginning, extremely intricate developments molded your body until it was complete with a brain that thinks, eyes that see, ears that hear, as well as many other specialized organs. This intricate process testifies to an intelligent Creator and Organizer. The book *The First Nine Months* describes the beginning of this remarkable process:

"When the sperm nucleus reaches the egg nucleus these two lie side by side as their content is combined. In this half hour an immeasurable number of traits of the new baby are decided within the pin-point egg."[200]

When these two cells unite, the plans are drawn up within the genetic DNA for an entire new human, and that in a matter of minutes!

Evolutionists have no satisfactory explanation for the marvelous, purposive processes by which a human body, or any organism, is able to duplicate itself and form intricate organs. Evolutionist Sir James Gray acknowledges this in *Science Today*. He speaks of a "predetermined plan," and a "directive principle," saying:

"The whole process seems much more like the development of organized structure from a relatively simpler system. The molecules of protein and fat in the yoke appear to be marshaled into position to form an orderly and highly complex system somewhat analogous to the process by which a house is built of bricks, wood and glass in accordance with a predetermined plan. . . . The machine seems to operate, in other words, in a highly purposive way and the term 'organizer' has been applied to it. . . . There seems to be some directive principle at work."[201]

The embryo of any living organism grows according to design, but the evolution theory cannot account for such intelligent direction and organization, whereas the Bible can. Evolutionist C. H. Waddington acknowledges that more than chemical processes are involved. Writing in his

1962 book *The Nature of Life,* he notes that cells are arranged "into organs with definite shapes and patterns," and admits:

> "I am afraid biologists have to confess that they still have hardly any notion of how this is done. It certainly must involve something more than purely chemical processes. . . .
>
> "It is, of course, only a beginning of understanding to say that the processes we are investigating force us to think in terms of theories which involve organization. Where does this organization come from?"[202]

Masterful design can also be seen in the remarkable arrangements made for housing a baby inside its mother. *Life*

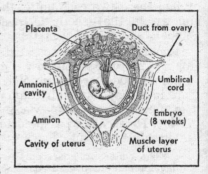

magazine of April 30, 1965, notes how these arrangements are carried out under the direction of recorded information within the first cell:

> "The fertilized egg cell contains in its tiny nucleus not only all the genetic instructions for building a human body, but also a complete manual on how to construct the complex protective armamentarium—amnion, umbilical cord, placenta and all—that makes possible the embryo's existence in the womb."[203]

The embryo requires this protective housing within the mother, for from the day of the egg's fertilization, it becomes foreign material. And ordinarily a person's immunological defenses would reject such a foreign growth. But the fertilized egg is able to circumvent these defenses. How appropriate it was for David to credit the Creator for this protective housing by saying: "You kept me screened off in the belly of my mother"! (Psalm 139:13) Thus the Bible states what is in harmony with the facts.

As an initial step to this screening off, one of the first instructions that are issued by the DNA is for the making of what are called trophoblast cells. These are produced for the initial purpose of building a little nest for the embryo in the uterus, or womb. The *Life* article explains:

> "The wall of the uterus is a thick, spongy material. The trophoblast cells dig right into it, destroying the uterine cells, taking nourishment from the blood and passing it along to sustain the first embryonic cells. Then they use the scar tissue from the healing wound they have inflicted as a temporary protective capsule for the still-microscopic parasite.
>
> "The uterus must protect itself against the further incursions of the aggressive trophoblast cells. Exactly how it does this is a mystery, because no other part of the body can do it. . . .
>
> "Once the embryo is firmly implanted, it starts secreting a hormone that helps keep the uterine lining in place for the rest of the embryo's stay. Without this hormone, menstruation would occur and the embryo would not survive."[204]

Who but an intelligent Creator could have seen the need for such provisions? Certainly unintelligent cells operating on blind chance could not have seen it. But when the embryo is screened off within the mother's womb, how does it obtain nourishment? How does it breathe, give off wastes and perform other necessary functions? By means of the amazing placenta:

> "Over the course of days, weeks and months, the embryo becomes firmly rooted in the uterine

wall, and the trophoblast cells develop into the placenta. A dynamic organ, the placenta changes constantly along with the embryo's changing requirements. It can perform tasks normally reserved for the lungs, liver, kidneys, intestines and endocrine glands, among its other miscellaneous accomplishments. . . .

"As a substitute lung, the placenta extracts oxygen from the mother's blood and deposits it in the blood of the embryo. The placenta brings in nutrients of all kinds from the mother's blood, often predigesting the dissolved food for the embryo en route. The placenta is so efficient that within an hour or two after the mother takes nourishment the embryo gets some too. . . . The placenta also manufactures vital hormones for the mother to make up for some of the things it takes away."[205]

Only after performing many miraculous tasks does the placenta die, and following the birth of the child, it is discharged from the mother as afterbirth. The entire process is summed up this way: "In the 266 days from conception to birth, the single fertilized egg cell becomes a staggeringly complex organization of some 200 million cells, having increased the original weight a billionfold."[206]

Evolution cannot account for such a marvelously purposive process. Yet, the Bible does by giving credit to a superior intelligence, a superior organizer, God the Creator. It harmonizes with the facts that where there is design there must be a designer and that, the more intricate a thing is, the more intelligent its maker must be. Notice how accurately David was inspired to show that the procedure was established by God: "Your eyes saw even the embryo of me, and in your book all its parts were down in writing." (Psalm 139:16) All the parts were "written" or locked in the DNA by God in the beginning.

But man is only one of God's creations. There are many others that testify to the existence of an intelligent Creator.

ANIMALS TESTIFY TO EXISTENCE OF CREATOR

When comparing man's inventions with the remarkable endowments of animals and insects, computer-scientist Dr. W. S. McCulloch was moved to remark: "Actually, computers are clumsy, stupid beasts . . . They haven't the brains of a retarded ant."[207] And *Natural History* of November 1961 said: "The nervous system of a single starfish, with all its various nerve ganglia and fibers, is more complex than London's telephone exchange."[208]

Not only does this complex organization testify to a master Organizer, but so does the fact that animals are endowed with a natural ability to apply physical laws, their accomplishments often defying attempts of humans to duplicate them. The flyleaf of the recent book *Bionics the Science of 'Living' Machines,* observes:

> "Engineers are taking cue after cue from the functions of living animals. The name of this fascinating 'copycat science' is bionics, a word so new that most dictionaries haven't listed it yet. . . .
>
> "Consider the airplane wings modeled after birds' wings, speed indicators that take hints from a beetle's flight, computers that evolved from nerve-cell research, internally worn heart stimulators developed from the study of animal electricity, and TV tubes that copy a crab's eye; we see that man is more and more applying nature's principles to his own needs."[209]

One of many things man is seeking to learn is the secret of how creatures such as whales and dolphins can move through water many times

Artic tern's yearly migration covers 22,000 miles!

faster than was considered possible. The above book notes:

"To swim at the speeds they were obviously achieving, the dolphin and the whale were either superpowerful or they had achieved what the aerodynamic and hydrodynamic engineers call 'laminar flow.' In other words, the water they swim in must follow the contours of the creatures so closely that there are no disturbances at all. . . .

"For decades aeronautical engineers have sought for laminar flow, but with only partial success, despite complicated additional equipment coupled to airplane wings."[210]

Do you believe that these creatures achieved this ability by blind evolutionary chance? Is it not obvious that an intelligent Creator with a perfect understanding of physical laws designed their bodies? And since man learns from this, does not that show there had to be a teacher?

One of the greatest testimonies to God's creative genius is found in the amazing navigational instinct that He has placed in many varieties of animals. The 1964 book *Marvels and Mysteries of Our Animal World* discusses this remarkable ability in birds:

"Perhaps the most challenging mystery is how birds can find their way unerringly over thousands of miles of featureless ocean. During most of the year a species of shearwater wanders over the Pacific, from Japan to California and northward to the Aleutian Islands. Yet the birds arrive at their nesting grounds off the coast of Australia—millions of them darkening the sky—on the same day every year.

"How do they do it? . . . These birds were not following older birds but a far more ancient guidance system, an instinct acquired in the egg."[211]

Scientists acknowledge that animals cannot learn or figure out complex problems of navigation, since they do not have the power to reason as man does. Yet they can navigate by the stars! This knowledge was incorporated in the genetic material of the egg. Consider the results of experiments presented in the 1965 book *The Mysterious Senses of Animals*. The author writes:

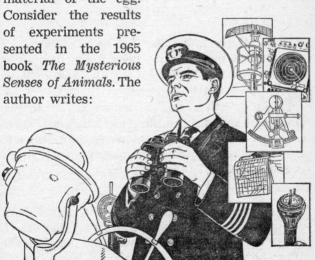

Man requires many navigation aids to accomplish what birds do by instinct. Radar, sextant, charts, compass and other aids show the wisdom of their originator. The far more efficient navigation system implanted in birds testifies to the greater wisdom of its Creator

"These experiments made it clear that blackcaps instinctively recognised individual constellations, 'knew' that they travelled across the sky during the night and also 'knew' the changes of the constellations with the changing seasons. . . .

"These small feathered astronomers can still navigate if only one or two stars are visible through the cloud cover. But if the sky is totally overcast, . . . they simply interrupt their migration . . .

"How do they acquire their extraordinary astronomical capacity? . . . the blackcap has inherited its knowledge of celestial geography and the course of the stars. Science still has no explanation to offer of how this instinctive knowledge of a subject as complicated as that of the constellations came to be embedded in an animal's germ plasm."[212]

It is utterly impossible for the knowledge of complicated mathematics needed for navigation to have evolved in birds by chance! Such facts do not harmonize with the evolution theory.

Evolution has no explanation for the instinctive wisdom of animals. But the Bible does. The wisdom everywhere manifested in living things testifies to the fact that they were designed by an intelligent Creator, by God, as the Bible shows.

BIBLE FITS FACTS

Thus, when we compare all the actual facts with the theory of evolution, we find that everywhere the theory is at odds with the facts. On the other hand, when we compare the teachings of the Bible about creation with the facts, we find that everywhere they are in accord with them.

As we have seen, the facts have proved that plants and animals reproduce only within their given kinds. Never do they evolve into another kind, nor have they ever done so. The fossil record bears this out. The marvelous DNA of living organisms shows that all have their own 'blueprints.' The fact that basic kinds cannot cross but are sterile also verifies the law of reproduction within kinds. The Bible's account of creation in Genesis chapter one harmonizes with these facts by stating that all living things were created "according to their kinds."

Whereas evolution cannot account for the beginning of life, the Bible can. All biological research shows that life comes only from life, verifying the principle of biogenesis. The Bible account in Genesis reveals God to be the source of all other life and is, therefore, in harmony with the facts of biogenesis. Psalm 36:9 identifies God as the life-giver: "For with you is the source of life."

The facts show that man, with a high brain capacity, suddenly "exploded" on the world scene. He made rapid advancement, so that civilization too "exploded." Ancient languages were also highly developed. The first two chapters of Genesis are in harmony with this, showing man to have been created with high intellect and language capability.

The facts show that within relatively recent times a disaster of unprecedented proportions struck the earth, resulting in the extermination of millions of living things, entombing many in icy graves. Even the weather changed drastically. The Bible account of a global flood that wiped out vast numbers of living things "that were on the dry ground" accounts for this.—Genesis 7:22.

The facts show that the earth is older than the claim made by some religions who mistakenly think it was created in a week of twenty-four-hour days. By leaving the time indefinite, Genesis 1:1 allows for a great time period before the six creative periods began that were much longer than twenty-four hours each. And the nearly 6,000 years that the Bible gives for man's total period of existence is verified by the records man has left.

So by comparing the known facts, free from speculations, with the Bible, it can be seen that the Biblical record about the beginning of life is true. And by identifying an intelligent Creator as the cause behind living things, it puts itself in harmony with the observed facts that show that, the more complex something is, the more intelligent must be its maker.—Romans 1:20.

Therefore, honest seekers after truth must acknowledge that the evidence is overwhelming that man got here, not as a result of evolution, but by means of creation by God.

CHAPTER 11

Why Do So Many Believe Evolution?

HowevER, if the Bible record is in harmony with the facts that have been found, whereas evolution is not, why do so many people believe evolution? There are various reasons why it has been so widely accepted throughout the world.

A basic reason is that in school most people are taught evolution. They are exposed to it in their study of history, science, philosophy and even religion. School textbooks are usually written by evolutionists and most of the teachers believe evolution. As evolutionist Rostand acknowledged:

> "We are permeated, saturated, with the transformist idea ... We learned it in our schoolrooms. We keep repeating mechanically that life evolves, that living things are changed from one into another."[213]

This indoctrination for generation after generation is certain to have its effect, particularly since opposing arguments are rarely presented to students. As C. P. Martin, an evolutionist, of McGill University said of the many students he observed:

> "It is not that they are aware of the difficulties ... and esteem them of little weight or importance; they never heard of them and are amazed

at the bare possibility of the accepted theory being criticized."[214]

A closely related reason why evolution is widely accepted is that the weight of authority is brought to bear on its behalf. When leading scientists, educators and clergymen assert that evolution is a fact, and imply that only the ignorant refuse to believe it, how many laymen are going to contradict them? Particularly is this so if one's career in the scientific field is involved. In *Evolution, Creation and Science* a professor of biology wrote of this influence on students:

"The thing which repeatedly won them over to acceptance of the theory was sheer weight of authority on the part of scientists through a not always highly refined method of browbeating. All too frequently if the young aspirant was to keep face with more seasoned scientists, he was obliged to accept the evolution theory."[215]

Because so much has been written about evolution by so many "authorities" the ordinary person often feels that they must have proved it to be so. But *Modern Science and Christian Faith* observes:

"A look at one of the large volumes on evolution impresses one that surely the subject is proved; but on reading it one finds data on genetic experiments, cytological studies, fossils from far and near, comparisons of skeletons, etc., showing slight changes in some species and great stability in others. The result is that before one is through one has gone off into a number of interesting side lanes and has lost sight of the usual definition of evolution. But the tendency on the part of the reader is to feel that a man who can cite so much that actually has been observed must be correct in his main thesis, and to forget the fact that the data do not all support his thesis."[216]

Still another reason for evolution's acceptance is the failure of orthodox religion in both practice and doctrine. The abuses, the intolerance and cruelty of various religions down through the ages have alienated many from God and the Bible. When thinking persons observe clergy support for dictators such as was given to Hitler and Mussolini, they withdraw from God and the Bible.

False religion's conflicting doctrines further this alienation. Such pagan ideas as eternal torment, that God will roast persons in a literal hellfire forever, taught in the name of God, are repugnant to reasoning persons. So they abandon religion altogether. The vacuum thus created is often filled later by evolution, agnosticism and atheism.

Because of false religious teachings, some persons believe that the Bible, God's Word, teaches things contrary to scientific fact. For example, some religions erroneously say the Bible teaches that the earth was created in six twenty-four-hour days. But scientific facts have proved the earth to be much older than this would indicate. Consequently the inclination is to discredit the Bible because of misunderstanding its teachings. They turn to evolution, not realizing that the Bible does not teach that the earth was created in six twenty-four-hour days.

In the book *The Biblical Flood and the Ice Epoch* we find an excuse or motive for believing evolution that few evolutionists would admit. It states: "If man is created, then this implies he was created for a purpose, which in turn is suggestive of man's responsibility to his Maker."[217] The desire to be free from such responsibility has turned many to evolution and atheism. This is noted in *Report* of

June 1966 in the article "Confession of a Professed Atheist: Aldous Huxley." Huxley stated:

> "I had motives for not wanting the world to have meaning; consequently assumed that it had none, and was able without any difficulty to find satisfying reasons for this assumption . . . For myself, as, no doubt, for most of my contemporaries, the philosophy of meaninglessness was essentially an instrument of liberation. The liberation we desired was simultaneously liberation from a certain political and economic system and liberation from a certain system of morality. We objected to the morality because it interfered with our sexual freedom."[218]

The prevalence of wickedness is undoubtedly an important reason why many others turn to belief in evolution. For centuries there has been much wickedness. Crime is growing at a frightening pace. Warfare, sickness and death plague mankind. Many persons cannot understand why God permits all of this to come upon the human family. Who or what is responsible? How could a good God allow bad to exist? Why does he not stop it? Because of not knowing the answers to such questions, many conclude that either there is no God or, if he exists, he does not take a direct hand in earth's affairs. Some think he is dead. So, since evolution appears to make the existence of God unnecessary, they accept it.

Obviously, the many questions regarding wickedness require answering.

CHAPTER 12

Who or What Was Responsible for Man's Wickedness?

THE history of the human family is not a particularly pleasant one, because of man's inhumanity to man. Over and over again individual or collective acts of wickedness have plunged large segments of humankind into brutality and bloodshed. As man's inventiveness has progressed, so has his capacity to cause grief.

In all this record of wickedness, the innocent, decent people all too often suffer. They are frequently victims of violence, perhaps losing homes, loved ones, or their own lives. You may or may not have experienced these things personally. Yet mental suffering due to injustices, unkindness and disloyalty may produce even greater misery, which you most likely have experienced.

Thinking men and women have wondered why this is so. Sooner or later they ask questions such as the following: Who or what was responsible for man's wickedness? If there is a God, why does he permit it? Will wickedness ever end?

WHO CAN PROVIDE THE ANSWERS?

Philosophers and religious leaders throughout the ages have pondered the problem of wickedness.

131

Yet their accumulated views are conflicting. As the book *The Basic Teachings of the Great Philosophers* says:

> "One philosopher will offer his solution and many will hail it as *the* answer. But it will not be long before another philosopher will discover and point to errors in his pattern, will reveal gaps and distortions, and will propose a somewhat different solution, one which seems to him more nearly perfect."

Why is this so? Because, as the same book comments, even a great philosopher "does not fashion a perfect picture. Only a God who knows all experiences of all men and can detect the finest relations can weave a perfect pattern. No philosopher, however great, is such a God."[219]

The fundamental truth of that cannot be denied. No man, of himself, however wise, can answer the questions regarding wickedness and why God permits it. But, then, who can? Why not give Jehovah God an opportunity to give his answer?

Consider this for a moment: If you wanted to know the views of someone, would it not be best to go to him and listen to what he has to say instead of listening to what others say his views are? Then, since it is, as some say, God the Creator who permits wickedness, it would only be fair and right to listen to the explanation that God provides.

Where does God provide this information? Surely we cannot think that God, after creating man, would leave humankind without an inspired record that would reveal the true history of his dealings with mankind and his view of things. He has provided such a record. The Christian apostle Paul, a God-fearing man writing under the guidance of the Creator, stated:

"All Scripture is inspired of God and beneficial for teaching, for reproving, for setting things straight, for disciplining in righteousness, that the man of God may be fully competent, completely equipped for every good work."—2 Timothy 3:16, 17.

There are still millions of people who believe that the Holy Scriptures, the Bible, is the inspired Word of God, that it is the Creator's communication to those of mankind who want to know about him and his purposes. Why not take a little time to look into that communication, written under the guidance of God, to find the answers as to who or what was responsible for wickedness, why God permits it, and what the future holds?

To begin with, let us examine how God created man, and the qualities with which man was endowed. This will aid us in determining how wickedness could ever arise within the human family in the first place.

MAN CREATED FREE

Would you like someone to dictate your every move in life? Would you appreciate it if someone scheduled your every living minute and then forced you never to deviate from that course by even a hairbreadth?

Or do you prefer to have the freedom to choose what kind of work you will do, where you will live, what you will eat, what you will wear, and what you will do with your leisure time?

The answers to those questions are obvious. No balanced human wants to lose complete control of his life. This can be seen even on a national scale where people are dominated by harsh, dictatorial governments. These oppressive governments stifle happiness and initiative. They also cause such pressures of resentment to build up that often an outbreak is made for freedom.

This desire for freedom is no accident. The Bible tells us that, in addition to life, God gave his first human creation, whom he named Adam, a most precious gift. That marvelous gift was free moral agency. Man was not to be a human robot, an automaton. He was endowed with the ability of individual choice. For instance, the ancient nation of Israel was told: "Choose for yourselves today whom you will serve."—Joshua 24:15; Genesis 1:26-28.

If the Creator had purposed for humans to be merely automatons, machinelike, he would not have equipped them with intellectual powers, powers of perception, judgment, decision and reason. As a robot, man would no more have need for such mental faculties than would a piece of machinery or a vegetable.

WHAT HUMAN PERFECTION MEANS

God created the first man, Adam, and also the first woman, Eve, perfect, that is, complete, without a defect in their physical organism. But did this perfection mean that they could do nothing but good? No, for while perfect, complete in their mental and physical faculties, they still had freedom of choice.

Their perfection did not mean they could do everything. They could not live in outer space without oxygen, nor could they stay underwater without special equipment. Also, they had to eat food and drink liquids to stay alive. They were perfect, but within the limits of humankind.

Similarly, their perfection did not mean that they knew everything, because all knowledge did not come automatically with their creation. It was not to be an instinct such as animals are endowed with to a certain degree. Whereas the animals cannot progress beyond a fixed point with their learning, man was given the capacity to improve on his knowledge by being able to learn continually.

In fact, even of Jesus Christ, the Bible says: "Although he was a Son [of God], he learned obedience." (Hebrews 5:8) So under God's direction Adam could learn many things. He could continue to build on this knowledge for his benefit and the benefit of all the human family that would issue from him. But he too had to learn obedience.

As a free moral agent he could meditate on what was wrong, if he chose to do so, and allow that to motivate him to wrong action. The Bible says: "Each one is tried by being drawn out and enticed by his own desire. Then the desire, when it has become fertile, gives birth to sin." Or Adam could choose obedience. So his perfection did not mean he was unable to entertain a wrong suggestion and could not make the decision for entertaining wrong desires and of violating God's law. —James 1:14, 15.

That Adam's individual will and personal choice, rather than physical perfection, were the determining factors in his conduct is evident. If we were to insist that a perfect man could not willfully take a wrong course where a moral issue was involved, should we not also logically argue that an *imperfect* creature could not willfully take a *right* course in the same situation? Yet today some imperfect creatures *do* take a right course on moral issues involving obedience to God's laws, even choosing to suffer persecution rather than change from such a course; while at the same time others deliberately engage in doing what they know is wrong. Thus not all *wrong* actions can be excused by human imperfection. The deciding factors are the individual's will and choice. In the same way, it was not human perfection alone that would guarantee *right* action by the first man, but, rather, his own will and choice motivated by love for his God and for what is right.

GOD'S GUIDANCE VITAL

For his own good, man needed God's guidance and direction. The reason why is so vital, so fundamental, that unless man appreciated its significance, he would come into grave difficulty. It is this: *Man was not made to live or govern independently of God.*

God did not give man the right or the ability either to live or to govern his affairs successfully without Him. The freedom given man was relative. It was to be maintained within proper limits,

limits that would work for man's good and contribute to his happiness. That is why God inspired his prophet Jeremiah to write: "I well know, O Jehovah, that to earthling man his way does not belong. It does not belong to man who is walking even to direct his step. Correct me, O Jehovah." It also explains why the Bible counsels: "Trust in Jehovah with all your heart and do not lean upon your own understanding."—Jeremiah 10:23, 24; Proverbs 3:5.

So while man was perfect as a physical organism, he needed the guidance of his God and Creator to live peacefully, happily, successfully and to manage his affairs properly. If he ever stopped accepting divine guidance and direction, his mind and intellect, though perfect, could no more resist deterioration spiritually than could his perfect body if deprived of organic food. Man's positive dependence on spiritual food, that is, the counsel and instructions from God, was not in the least degree less vital than his dependence on material food. This fact is declared both in the Mosaic law and by Jesus Christ. (Deuteronomy 8:3; Matthew 4:4) If man were to refuse to accept the guidance of Almighty God over his life, then chaos would inevitably result in the ranks of humankind.

Thus if man stopped obeying and trusting God and depended on his own wisdom alone, he would lose the peace and happiness that would have been his. Has this occurred? Well, look about you in the earth today. What do you see? Do you see the entire human family of free moral agents united in a bond of love, happy and thrilled with each day of life? Or, instead, do you see the earth filled with unhappy people who are suffering, divided, perplexed and confused? The evidence of history and of our own time is that the latter is true. Man has, beyond any doubt, lost genuine happiness and is suffering from widespread wickedness. The reason why is that he has abandoned the guidance of God.

THE WRONG CHOICE

With the freedom to choose, our first parents, Adam and his wife Eve, chose to refuse God's guidance. They entertained wrong desires that led to disobedience. They broke God's plainly stated regulation for them. This was nothing less than outright rebellion against their Creator. —Genesis 2:16, 17; 3:1-6.

By choosing to rebel against God they had to get along without his blessing and guidance. Since that is what they chose, that is what God granted them. Their rejection of God as their ruler meant that their Creator would no longer sustain them in perfection. Instead of their living forever on earth, as was initially their prospect, the process of degeneration would set in, with their physical organism breaking down and ultimate death being inevitable.

God told rebellious Adam what would happen to him for his disobedience, and we still see the effects of that adverse judgment. God said: "In the sweat of your face you will eat bread until you return to the ground, for out of it you were taken. For dust you are and to dust you will return." (Genesis 3:19) Here was a universal law just as binding as the law of gravity: sin produces death. Adam's disobedience set mankind on a downward course, because he could not produce offspring free from the physical effects of his sin. It is written: "That is why, just as through one man sin entered into the world and death through sin, and thus death spread to all men because they had all sinned."—Romans 5:12.

IS GOD TO BLAME FOR MAN'S WRONGS?

The calamity that came upon Adam and Eve was their own fault. God had clearly warned them of the result if they failed to obey his righteous law; yet they chose a course of lawlessness toward God. But what about all the wickedness committed in the thousands of years since then? Whose fault is that? Is it God's?

The Bible shows that the blame for wickedness lies in two places, one of which is man himself. Let us examine his responsibility first.

When a person commits a crime, who is punished? Would it be just to punish the innocent victim and let the criminal go free? No, it is the criminal who is responsible and who should be punished. The innocent one cannot be held responsible for what he did not do. In like manner, we must not hold God responsible for acts of wickedness. We must put the blame where it belongs, on those who commit such acts.

Remember, Adam's descendants have been born since his sin and so suffer the effects it brought. Nevertheless, they are free moral agents. They are free to choose to do right or wrong, just as Adam was. Though by their imperfection they do commit many errors, yet, when they *choose* to do wrong, it is their own fault. That is why the Bible, at Deuteronomy 32:5, says: "They have acted ruinously on their own part; they are not [God's] children, the defect is their own."

True, many innocent people who try to do good are victimized by the wicked deeds of others. But, here again, the innocent ones must appreciate that it is the wicked criminal who is responsible for their hurt, not God. Furthermore, God is not oblivious to their plight. We will later see how he will deliver persons from their unfortunate circumstances and erase any hurt they have unjustly received.

TENDENCY TO SHIFT BLAME

So, then, much of the wickedness perpetrated for the past thousands of years can be traced to man's own doing. He cannot shift the responsibility for his own wrongdoing onto God, although this is what many try to do. Why, even Adam, when called to account for his transgression, tried to avoid responsibility by saying the cause for his dereliction was "the woman whom *you* [God] gave to be with me." (Genesis 3:12) However, it was not God who was in the wrong. He did nothing unloving or unjust. On the contrary, he had been very loving to give man life to begin with, to place him in a beautiful gardenlike area of the earth, and to give him a lovely wife as well as dominion over the lower animal creation.

It was Adam who committed the wrong, who acted wickedly. The Bible assures us that "Adam was not deceived." He was competent to make a choice, and because he chose what was bad he and his descendants have suffered.—1 Timothy 2:14.

Throughout history humans have followed Adam's course by tending to blame God for the evil that befalls them. In the case of some, they follow the dictates of their own selfish will and violate God's laws, bringing trouble and unhappiness upon themselves. They may feel that God is at fault for not preventing their misfortune. But he is not to blame. They suffer for their own misdeeds.

While there can be no doubt that some persons are genuinely perplexed and are seeking to know the reason for God's permission of wickedness, the sincerity of many others who strongly criticize God is open to question. Are they really honest in their insistence that God is at fault because he did not forcibly prevent man's deviation from righteousness at its very inception? Where, then, is the proof that they as individuals personally desire stricter control by God or where is the proof that even a sizable majority of mankind at any time has manifested a desire that God use his power to inhibit their ways or block them in their pursuits, when these are wrong? If they do not want this for themselves, why should we believe they really would want it for our first parents? Are they not like the person who heartily cheers law enforcement but reacts resentfully when a traffic policeman gives him a ticket?—Ezekiel 18:29-32.

When entire nations behave criminally, can they blame God if suffering or disaster befalls them? If they cast out God's commandments, can they blame him for their troubles or for his not coming to their aid? They are to blame, not God, for the unhappiness and suffering they bring upon their people.

SICKNESS AND DISEASE

But what about all the suffering that comes from sickness and disease? Even persons who try to do good get sick, through no fault of their own. An infant, for example, has done nothing to account for an illness that might cripple it, or even take its life. Why does it have to suffer?

In regard to all sickness, disease and painful suffering, we must put the blame where it belongs, on the rebellion of Adam and Eve. They brought about the circumstances that have caused our bodies to be imperfect and to function improperly.

They could not produce offspring free of their imperfection. Job 14:4 declares: "Who can produce someone clean out of someone unclean? There is not one."—Psalm 51:4; Luke 5:18-25.

If, as an example, certain human parents ignore the divine law and live immorally, and so contract venereal disease, whose fault is it if their children are born physically or mentally impaired? It is the fault of such "unclean" parents.

So, too, our first parents became "unclean," imperfect, prone to sickness and death. They could pass on to their offspring only what they themselves had. Being their descendants, all mankind is susceptible to sickness, disease, deformities and death. That is why even infants suffer. Rebellion against God by the first pair accounts in large measure for the unhappy state of the human family today.

FALSE RELIGION SHARES BLAME

The traditional religions have often attributed to God the calamities that man experiences. They have taught that disasters, poverty, filth and ignorance are God's will for the people. In some countries religious tradition claims that a cow is more sacred than a man, and that, even though the man may be starving, the cow cannot be used for food. God's Word, however, says it can. (Genesis 9:3; 1 Corinthians 10:25) Such religious teachings, which are not based on God's Word, increase man's difficulties while, at the same time, blaming God for them.

There are other religions that justify the wars among political rulers of the world, even blessing the guns, encouraging soldiers to kill one another, although they may belong to the same religion. God has nothing to do with such wars and has no part in them. Instead, he is going to make wars cease permanently.—Psalm 46:9; Isaiah 2:4.

God is not to blame for man's inhumanity to man, even though some religions falsely claim that he is. He is not responsible for the fiendish inquisitions instituted by religious leaders during the "dark ages." He never authorized such horrible crimes. With regard to the pagan practice in ancient Israel of burning children to false gods, Jehovah God stated: "They have built the high places of Topheth, which is in the valley of the son of Hinnom, in order to burn their sons and their daughters in the fire, *a thing that I had not commanded and that had not come up into my heart.*" When God condemns what men do, he is certainly not responsible for it.—Jeremiah 7:31.

Wrongs committed in the name of religion are especially disgusting to God. Jesus Christ said to the religious leaders in his day: "Woe to you, scribes and Pharisees, hypocrites! because you resemble whitewashed graves, which outwardly indeed appear beautiful but inside are full of dead men's bones and of every sort of uncleanness. In that way you also, outwardly indeed, appear righteous to men, but inside you are full of hypocrisy and lawlessness." (Matthew 23:27, 28) The same can be said today of religious leaders who piously appear to serve God but whose actions discredit him.

The lawless deeds of false religion cannot be blamed on God. The mere fact that a religious movement claims a long history of hundreds of years does not mean it is doing God's will when it gains conversions by the sword. When it does things that are contrary to the clearly expressed will of God in his Word, then the suffering it causes is strictly of its own making. God is no party to it.

However, it was previously stated that the blame for wickedness lies in two places. Man has brought much of it upon himself by freely choosing what is bad. But blame also lies elsewhere.

WHO IS PRINCIPALLY RESPONSIBLE?

When criminals operate behind a well-planned organizational setup, with numerous fronts that appear to be quite law-abiding, it is difficult for the man in the street to penetrate the deception or believe that the unseen master schemers even exist. The principal wicked one whose criminal actions and policies have helped to bring untold miseries upon the human family also works behind the scenes. But we do not have to be in ignorance of him, because God has exposed his workings so that we can know about him for our own information and protection.

God, in his own Word, identifies the creature that has been the chief inspirer of wickedness. It was he who corrupted Eve's integrity, and induced her to rebel against her righteous Creator.

He is an invisible wicked spirit creature. His invisibility should not make you doubt his existence. The existence of microorganisms as disease-causing factors was once doubted because they could not be seen with the naked eye, but that was not a valid reason for doubting their existence. The same can be said about this spirit creature.

The precise cause of cancer is still unknown, but scientists do not simply shrug their shoulders and say, "Cancer is caused by cancer." They are certain that a causative factor exists. So, too, wickedness is not just caused by wickedness. It had a start, and its spread through mankind to plague-like proportions also indicates an active infecting source.

Radio impulses are invisible, but we know they exist because of the effect they cause in a radio receiver. We believe that radio impulses exist although we cannot see them with the naked eye. We know they have a source even when they come from the starry heavens. There are many such things that are invisible to the naked eye but that we can discern by the results they produce. So, too, the existence of the invisible one who introduced wickedness can be discerned by the results of his activity. We also have the Bible's testimony about him.

In the third chapter of the Bible book of Genesis we read of a serpent's speaking to the first woman Eve and telling her the first lie. God the Creator had told man that disobedience to his laws would mean certain death. This serpent said the opposite: "You positively will not die." In fact, the serpent went on to tell Eve: "Your eyes are bound to be opened and you are bound to be like God." Eve believed this lie and disobeyed God. Then she persuaded her husband to join her in rebellion.—Genesis 3:4, 5.

But who actually lied to Eve and instilled the idea of rebellion in her mind? Was it a mere reptile, a snake that has no speech organs? No, there was someone behind the serpent making it appear as if the snake were talking. We know that a skilled ventriloquist can make an animal or even a dummy appear to talk, when actually it is not. How much more easily could an invisible, intelligent spirit creature do so! The Bible, at Revelation 12:9, identifies that powerful spirit creature, speaking of him as "the original serpent." He is clearly identified as being Satan the Devil.

Here, then, is man's hated enemy and the one chiefly responsible for the earth-wide spread of wickedness.

SUCCUMBED TO WRONG IDEAS

Obviously, the God 'whose activity is perfect' would not deliberately bring into existence a wicked creature. (Deuteronomy 32:4) That would be contrary to his love for righteousness. —Psalms 5:4-6; 15:1, 2.

The invisible creature that introduced rebellion to Adam and Eve was perfect, without defect, but, like Adam and Eve, he was a free moral agent, able to choose good or bad. It was by his entertaining a wrong desire that he chose a course of wickedness. For example, a person in someone else's home may see a watch lying on a table. The possibility of his picking that watch up and putting it into his pocket is evident, but he may not even consider it; or, if the idea does suggest itself, he may immediately dismiss it. But if he retains the idea and allows a wrong desire to develop and grow, the process toward wrongdoing will have been initiated, and he may well commit the wicked act of stealing.

The same process caused a perfect spirit creature to become Satan the Devil. The possibility of using the human pair for his own purposes rather than that indicated by God was there. He not only considered it but also failed to dismiss it from his mind. He entertained this wrong desire and it led to wrongdoing, sin. So he made himself the chief force for wickedness. God was not responsible for the course he chose.

Responsibility for worldwide wickedness, then, rests primarily with Satan the Devil. He is the one principally to blame, as the Bible explicitly shows at 1 John 5:19: "The whole world is lying in the power of the wicked one." But the Devil is not the only invisible wicked creature. The Holy Scriptures make it clear that Christians "have a fight, not against blood and flesh, but against . . . the wicked spirit forces in the heavenly places." (Ephesians 6:12) So other wicked spirits, demons, are also responsible for the spread of wickedness. —Revelation 12:9.

But why did spirit creatures of God turn themselves into demons? Again it was a matter of wrong desire. The Bible informs us that certain spirit creatures left their assigned duties in the universe due to improper desires and willingly came under the leadership of their fellow rebel, the Devil. (Genesis 6:2; 2 Peter 2:4; Jude 6) These rebellious spirits have caused all manner of woes for mankind.

RESPONSIBILITY FOR PRESENT WOES

The Bible foretold that there would be a vast increase in every kind of crime in our day. It shows the reason for it to be the fact that Satan and his demons have been confined to the vicinity of the earth now: "Woe for the earth and for the sea, because the Devil has come down to you, having great anger, knowing he has a short period of time."—Revelation 12:12.

Other prophecies concerning the time in which we live, such as at Second Timothy chapter 3, and Matthew chapter 24, tell of world woes resulting from the spread of wickedness. They have come to be because men have opened their minds to demon inspiration and guidance. Knowing that they have "a short period of time," Satan and his demon hordes are viciously trying to drag down with them as many humans as they can overreach and coerce into rebelling against God.—Revelation 16:13, 14.

A principal means of doing this on a mass scale is wicked governments that have the power to regiment the masses of people and compel them to violate God's good laws. It is with good reason that the Holy Bible speaks of human governments under the symbol of cruel, unloving, destructive wild beasts. (Daniel 8:1-8, 20-25) As noted in the thirteenth chapter of Revelation, Satan himself has been the one who has empowered these ruling authorities. He is the "god of this system of things." (2 Corinthians 4:4) It is he who has instigated their oppressive rule, inspired their horrible wars and moves them to persecute God-fearing persons for obeying God's laws. He has caused these governments to take to themselves rights and powers of rulership that only God can safely and wisely exercise. He has promoted all the blasphemies against God that those national sovereignties have uttered. Thus, when we see nations at one another's throats today, it is not because God is their ruler. It is because they are part of Satan's organization.—Luke 4:5-8.

So we see that the terrible woes and widespread wickedness that have brought suffering to mankind are not from Almighty God. They are mainly caused by mankind's great enemies—Satan the Devil and his hordes of demons.

While the self-made Satan the Devil induced Adam and Eve to join in his wicked rebellion against God's authority, we must remember that he could not compel them to do wrong. Adam and Eve were not so weak and incompetent that they were unable to resist. The Bible says: "Oppose the Devil, and he will flee from you." Our first parents were completely capable of telling this lying spirit creature that they would not go along with him. Centuries later the perfect man Jesus proved that this could be done, for he said to Satan: "Go away, Satan! For it is written, 'It is Jehovah your God you must worship, and it is to him alone you must render sacred service.'"—James 4:7; Matthew 4:10.

Had Adam and Eve said to Satan what Jesus did, the human family would not find itself plagued with acts of wickedness today. Hence, while Satan was the chief culprit, responsible for the eventual death of Adam and Eve, they were also responsible, for they could have turned aside his wrong suggestions. But they did not, and because they did not they caused all their offspring, including us, to inherit imperfection, which brought with it sickness, sorrow and death.—Hebrews 2:14.

But why has God permitted wickedness *for so long?* That is the question that troubles many people.

CHAPTER 13

Why Has Wickedness Been Permitted for So Long?

ALMOST six thousand years of human history have produced a long record of suffering, tears and death. The sympathetic mind cannot but feel for the tormented generations of the past, as well as for our own.

Why has God permitted all this for so long? His Word gives definite and satisfying answers. It tells us of various issues that needed settling. It shows us, too, that in God's unsurpassed wisdom he is following a course that will work out for the greatest good for all creation.

Are you sincerely interested in learning why God has permitted wickedness to exist? Then appreciate that there are a number of interrelated reasons, and that only a full explanation truly satisfies. If your own reputation were at stake, would you feel that others were fair if they demanded an explanation but then walked away almost as soon as you started to speak? Of course not. So, then, let us consider carefully the reasons for God's permission of wickedness.—Proverbs 18:13.

NOT AN ISSUE OF SUPERIOR FORCE

When rebellion broke out in the beginning, God did not delay in taking action. The third chapter of Genesis shows that God promptly called to account all who were involved and passed sentence on them in harmony with his righteous law. (Genesis 3:8-19) However, God did not immediately carry out the death penalty against Adam and Eve, but, with a view to the future blessing of their then unborn offspring, allowed them to produce children. (Genesis 22:18; Galatians 3:8) We should be grateful that he did, otherwise we would never have been born.

In passing judgment on that rebel spirit creature who had made a Devil out of himself by lying against God, Jehovah stated in symbolic language his purpose for the future. (Genesis 3:15) The Devil would not be immediately destroyed but would be allowed to exist for a period of time that God himself determined, in order to settle *for all time* the issues that had been raised there in Eden.

Had the issue been simply one of superior power, it could have been settled by a fight to the finish right then. But there is no evidence that Satan challenged God's strength. Rather, the account in Genesis shows that Satan raised a moral issue. He disputed God's truthfulness, and, as revealed later in the Bible, he also called into question the integrity of all God's creatures toward God's universal sovereignty. (Genesis 3:1-5; Job 1:7-12) The settling of such issues in a satisfying way would require time, as the immediate application of overwhelming strength on God's part would not answer the moral questions raised.

A SET TIME

As we look back on the history of God's dealings with mankind as revealed in the Bible, it is clear that, though God did not tell those who were in rebellion against him how long he would tolerate wickedness, he himself did set a time limit. Centuries later he indicated that to his prophet Daniel in a message delivered by one of God's obedient spirit creatures. At that time, long before the start of our Common Era, he said concerning the end of this wicked system: "The end is yet for the time appointed."—Daniel 11:27.

Nearly six thousand years from Adam's rebellion until our day may seem like an extremely long period of time when viewed only from the standpoint of humans who live about seventy years. But, remember, it is God who set the time. Concerning his concept of time, the Bible tells us at Psalm 90:4: "A thousand years are in your eyes but as yesterday when it is past, and as a watch during the night." A year is a long time to a child who has lived only five years, but to a man who is sixty it is comparatively short. Likewise, to God, who lives for eternity, a thousand years is like a day. From his standpoint, his toleration of wickedness has not yet lasted six full days.

Certainly that has been no injustice to us. It is because of God's long-suffering that we have had opportunity to live at all, because all of us are descendants of Adam. And even under imperfect conditions life is cherished; yes, even in sickness we cling to it. But the fact that God did not cut short his long-suffering at some earlier time, but has allowed it to continue until our day, affords opportunity for more than a brief existence for us.

To help us appreciate this, the apostle Peter wrote: "Jehovah is not slow respecting his promise, as some people consider slowness, but he is patient with you because he does not desire any to be destroyed but desires all to attain to repentance. Furthermore, consider the patience of our Lord as salvation." (2 Peter 3:9, 15) So it becomes evident that God's long-suffering has worked for our blessing, not our harm.

Something else has been accomplished, too, and it is likewise for our benefit and the benefit of all creation now and in the unlimited future.

WOULD THE WAY OF REBELLION PRODUCE GOOD RESULTS?

During the past six thousand years the Devil and men alienated from God have had full opportunity to work out their wicked schemes. By his course of action Satan set himself up as a rival ruler, challenging God's rulership. By inducing men to serve him, he has become their ruler and their god. For that reason he is called in the Bible "the ruler of this world" and "the god of this system of things." (John 12:31; 2 Corinthians 4: 4) It is not just a few particularly wicked persons who come under his control; rather, the Bible says that "the whole world is lying in the power of the wicked one." (1 John 5:19) Also, by inducing other spirit creatures to follow his rebellious course he became "ruler of the demons."—Matthew 9:34.

Now, then, the question raised here is this: Would this way of rebellion prove successful? Would rulership that endeavored to ignore God ever bring lasting benefits to anyone? Would God's rulership of living creatures prove better for them all, or would Satan's rulership of creatures prove better? Would man's rule independent of God be better for him, or would man's subjection to God and his laws be better for mankind?

True, God could have wiped out the rebellion at its start, but *that would not have satisfactorily settled matters.* Therefore, God has permitted a full measure of time for Satan to build up his organization, and for independent men to arrive at their peak of material prosperity, scientific achievement and military might. In this way God has enabled all intelligent creation, both in the invisible spirit realm and here on earth, to see the consequences of rebellion.

What is the result? What has nearly six thousand years of rule by the Devil and by men alienated from God shown? Has the course of rebellion against God proved better for mankind? Has it brought them lasting happiness?

When the honest person ponders past history and the present tragic state of affairs in the world, he must realize how devoid of genuine progress the record is. All kinds of governments have been tried, but still man lacks security and enduring happiness. Can one speak of true progress when the arrow has been replaced by the atomic bomb, and when the world now staggers on the brink of another global war? What kind of progress is it when men send rockets to the moon but cannot live together in peace on earth? What good is it for man to build homes equipped with every convenience, only to have a family torn apart by divorce and delinquency? Are riots in the streets, destruction of property and life, and widespread lawlessness, something of which to be proud? Not at all! But they are all the fruitage of rule that endeavors to ignore God.

Surely God's long permission of rebellion and its resulting wickedness prove to all reasonable men that *satisfactory rule of earth's affairs is impossible apart from God.* That is what God told man in the beginning. That is the truth of the matter as we see by centuries of actual history. God has proved to be the truth teller.

The long time that has elapsed has proved the rule by rebellious men and wicked spirit creatures to be a dismal failure. It has proved that Satan has no right to rule anywhere, and that *men surely were not created with the ability to direct their affairs apart from the guidance of God.* Now, with the record of six thousand years of failure, never can it be said that the Creator did not allow sufficient time for rebels to experiment. Never can anyone rightfully claim: 'They did not get a chance.' Nor can anyone ever say: 'If only they had more time.' The allotted time has been ample to prove their failure. The way of rebellion has proved to be an absolute disaster! But God will not allow rebels to wreck this earth. Instead, for the benefit of decent people, he, in his due time, will "bring to ruin those ruining the earth." —Revelation 11:18.

LEGAL PRECEDENT ESTABLISHED

In thus allowing the Devil and rebellious men time to carry their schemes to their limit, God has taken a long-range view of matters, a view that would benefit creatures throughout eternity. Should the situation ever arise at any future time that any free moral agent abuses his freedom of choice and calls into question God's way of doing things, would it be necessary for God to grant him time to make good his theories or charges? Would God allow wickedness to exist again for thousands of additional years? Absolutely not!

Having on this occasion allowed rebels to continue for their allotted time of six thousand years, God will have established a clear legal precedent that can be applied anywhere in the universe and throughout all eternity. It will already have been amply proved that nothing that is out of harmony with Jehovah God can prosper, that no independent scheme of man or spirit can bring benefits, but that chaos will be the result. God will then be fully justified before all intelligent creatures in swiftly crushing any rebel. "The wicked ones he will annihilate."—Psalm 145:20; Romans 3:4.

Throughout eternity our planet, Earth, will bear a distinction that no other planet will enjoy. It will be the one where the issues were raised by rebellious men and spirit creatures, where they were settled, where the legal precedent was established that can be used as a touchstone everywhere else in the universe. It is not that the Earth may be the only planet to be inhabited. The Creator could choose to put inhabitants on thousands, millions, even billions of other planets in due time. But imagine the chaos that would be present in the universe if all such were permitted to rebel and work out their own ways! No such permission will be granted. That is why, even though the experience for us humans has been a painful one, it has been a beneficial one because of the issues that will be settled by it. Thus, God will have established once and *for all time* the legal precedent that can be used for the benefit and happiness of living creatures throughout the endless ages of time ahead of us.

SATAN PROVED A LIAR

In the days of the Oriental patriarch Job, about the sixteenth century B.C.E., it was made unmistakably clear that man's integrity toward God was also at issue. Jehovah said that there was no one like Job in the earth, yet the Devil sneered: "Is it for nothing that Job has feared God? Have not you yourself put up a hedge about him and about his house and about everything that he has all around? The work of his hands you have blessed, and his livestock itself has spread abroad in the earth. But, for a change, thrust out your hand, please, and touch everything he has and see whether he will not curse you to your very face." (Job 1:6-12) Yes, Satan boasted that he could turn all men away from God, even the one of whom God would say "there is no one like him in the earth."

Already Satan had been trying to prove his boast since Eden. Adam failed God, but men of faith such as Abel, Enoch and Noah proved faithful to God. They served him out of love, not for material gain. Job too declared: "Until I expire I shall not take away my integrity." (Job 27:5) Yet Satan, his mind warped by proud ambition, refused to slow down in his insane course. When the perfect man Jesus was on earth, Satan endeavored to bribe him to commit just one act that would be a breach of integrity to God. (Matt. 4:9-11) Even when slapped around by soldier guards and then nailed to a stake to die, Jesus held fast to his integrity. The Devil used his agents to put Jesus to death, but he could not induce him to become disloyal to God. (Philippians 2:8) By Jesus' maintaining integrity as a perfect human he proved that it was not impossible for Adam to have done so.

Satan has also brought pressure on those who are followers of Christ. (Luke 22:31) Down to our day he has 'waged war' with those "who observe the commandments of God and have the work of bearing witness to Jesus." (Revelation 12:17) These have been joined by "a great crowd, which no man was able to number, out of all nations and tribes and peoples and tongues," who, though living at a time of "great tribulation," give heart-felt thanks and praise to the Creator and to his Son. (Revelation 7:9, 10, 14) They appreciate that one of the issues involved in the rebellion of Satan was the moral issue of man's integrity. That is why, even under the most adverse circum-stances, they are glad to have a part in contribut-ing to the overwhelming evidence that God's way is right and that his creatures can exercise their free moral agency and maintain integrity to him. They do this out of love for what is right and not for material gain.

GOD'S NAME AND POWER PROCLAIMED

Because of his great love for mankind, God will bring an end to wickedness. He will bring an end to the rebellion of man and of wicked spirit crea-tures. The display of power that God will unleash at his set time, and the good it will accomplish, will be the talk of ages to come.

On an earth-wide, indeed, universal scale it will happen as it did in ancient Egypt when God told its haughty ruler: "For this cause I have kept you in existence, for the sake of showing you my power and in order to have my name declared in all the earth." (Exodus 9:16) When God smashed the proud, oppressive Egyptians and all their military might, the news of it spread far and wide. So great became God's fame because of the way he delivered the enslaved Israelites that a person living in distant Jericho years later said: "We have heard how Jehovah dried up the waters of the Red Sea from before you when you came out of Egypt, . . . Jehovah your God is God in the heavens above and on the earth beneath."—Joshua 2:9-11.

God's crushing of the wicked will be reason for

all intelligent creatures to make the same acknowledgment. Throughout the universe they will do so when God brings an end to oppression and wickedness. For all eternity righteous-hearted men and spirit creatures will recount what God did to rid the universe of wickedness and how he brought blessings to all who love and serve him. His name will be praised throughout heaven and earth when he settles accounts with Satan, the demons, and wicked people on earth. Then "they will have to know that [he is] Jehovah."—Ezekiel 38:23.

Proved for all time will be the fact that the way of rebellion against God does not work for the good of anyone. Satan will be revealed as the most monstrous liar of all time, and as no god to follow. The Creator, Jehovah God, will have been proved true and the one to whom we should give our obedience. Also, a legal precedent will have been established once and for all time for the benefit of all living, intelligent creatures. Obedience to God will have been proved to be the only worthwhile course!

But the question of prime consideration now is, When will God act to bring an end to wickedness? How much longer will he tolerate it? When will he destroy the whole wicked system that Satan has built up?

CHAPTER 14

How Much Longer Will It Be?

Aᴌᴌ honest-hearted men and women everywhere keenly desire to know when God will bring an end to wickedness. How much longer will it be?

In the first century of our Common Era, Jesus' disciples were keenly interested in this too. In fact, they pointedly asked him: "Tell us, When will these things be, and what will be the sign of your presence and of the conclusion of the system of things?" Since his second presence was to be invisible, spiritual, Jesus gave them visible signs that would combine to mark the period of the "time of the end," known also as the "last days." Persons living then would be able to recognize the significance of that period by these signs.—Matthew 24:3; Daniel 11:40.

The "last" of anything means the final part, the finish, the end. For example, the last day of the week means the final twenty-four hours that bring the week to a conclusion. Historians speak of "the last days of Pompeii" just before it was destroyed. So when the Bible speaks of the "last days," it has reference, not just to days of a week, but to a period of time marked by catastrophic events world wide. As 2 Timothy 3:1 stated: "In the last days critical times hard to deal with will be here." These "last days" would mean that all elements of Satan's system of things and rebellious mankind, the political, the military, the economic, the social and the religious, would be nearing a cataclysmic finish.

As the last day of a week has a definite beginning and a definite end, so the "last days" of this entire system of things have a definite beginning and a definite end. During this time the many distinguishing events enumerated by Jesus and other Bible writers would take place. They would happen within one generation to identify the "last days" clearly. They would be like the different lines that make up a person's fingerprint, a print that cannot belong to any other person. The "last days" contain their own unique grouping of marks, or events, forming a positive "fingerprint" that cannot belong to any other time period.

When the many factors are put together, what do we find? We find that the time of *our* generation, *our* day, is the one that is identified in the Bible as the "last days." In fact, we are actually living in the *final* part of that time. This can be compared, not just to the last day of a week, but, rather, to the last part of that last day.

When Jesus gave his prophecy about the "last days" he realized that many centuries would pass before he would come again, this time in Kingdom power, and bring an end to wickedness. During all this time he knew that men would fight many wars. That is why, before giving the visible evidences that would mark the "last days," he explained: "You are going to hear of wars and reports of wars; see that you are not terrified. For these things must take place, but the end is not yet." Such wars did occur during the nineteen hundred years down to our day.—Matthew 24:6.

"TIME OF THE END" BEGINS

Next, Jesus began enumerating the world-shaking events that would mark his invisible second presence and the fact that mankind had entered the "time of the end." Have we in this generation seen what Jesus said to look for? Yes, we have! Consider what he said: "Nation will rise against nation, and kingdom against kingdom." Following this he said "there will be great earthquakes, and in one place after another pestilences and food shortages."—Luke 21:10, 11.

What was Jesus telling his future followers to look for as a time marker for indicating the beginning of the "last days"? They were to look for a disastrous war the dimensions of which were unheard of in history, one that would be accompanied quickly by other disasters, such as disease, food shortages and earthquakes.

Which war was Jesus speaking about? World War I! It was the first war to fill the description he gave, for it included entire kingdoms, indeed, the entire world. Speaking of World War I, *Life* magazine stated: "It killed more men than any previous war, and it was the first war to suck in whole nations, including civilians."[220]

No previous war in history compared with it. It was so different that historians of that time called it The Great War, or The World War. It was by far the greatest war in history, the first of its kind. Of it, an encyclopedia states: "World War I took the lives of twice as many men as all major wars from 1790 to 1913 put together." It noted that total military casualties were over 37,000,000, and added: "The number of civilian deaths in areas of actual war totaled about 5,000,000. Starvation, disease, and exposure accounted for about 80 of every 100 of these civilian deaths. Spanish influenza, which some persons blamed on the war, caused tens of millions of other deaths."[221] World war! Pestilences! Food shortages! Just as Jesus foretold!

Yes, 1914 marked the "beginning of pangs of distress," as Jesus declared. (Matthew 24:8) It was the time marker indicating the start of the "last days." That it was a time marker is noted by news publications and outstanding men of the world. On the anniversary of World War I the London *Evening Star* commented that the conflict "tore the whole world's political setup apart. Nothing could ever be the same again. If we all get the nuclear madness out of our systems and the human race survives, some historian in the next century may well conclude that the day the world went mad was August 4, 1914."[222]

Indicating the tremendous change that the first world war made in human history, the New York *Times Magazine* said: "The first war . . . closed a long era of general peace and began a new age of violence in which the second war is simply an episode. Since 1914 the world has had a new character . . . Thus the first World War marks a turning point in modern history." [223]

Former chancellor of West Germany Konrad Adenauer spoke of the time "before 1914 when there was real peace, quiet and security on this earth—a time when we didn't know fear. . . . Security and quiet have disappeared from the lives of men since 1914. And peace? Since 1914, the Germans have not known real peace nor has much of mankind."[224] Similarly, former president of the United States Dwight D. Eisenhower said: "A deterioration has been going on since the first World War."[225]

Also, as Jesus foretold, after 1914 a series of earthquakes rocked the globe, causing more damage and casualties than ever before. In 1915, at Avezzano, Italy, 30,000 were killed. In 1920, 180,000 died in Kansu, China. In 1923, 143,000 perished in Japan. And earthquakes have continued to occur with frightening intensity, taking a toll of lives greater than in any other period of human history. Now almost every year sees a major tragedy due to earthquakes. Just since 1960 there have been devastating earthquakes in Morocco, Chile, Iran, Yugoslavia, Alaska, Turkey and other areas. Clearly they form another identifying mark of the "fingerprint" of these "last days" that tells us that wickedness will not continue much longer, for this system of things is nearing its end.

MORE TO COME

However, the events that took place in connection with World War I were, as Jesus said, only the "beginning of pangs of distress" of the "last days." Much more was to come that would further establish beyond any doubt that the system of things had entered its "time of the end." Much more did come.

Note what one history source says: "World War I and its aftermath led to the greatest economic depression in history during the early 1930's. The consequences of the war and the problems of adjustment to peace led to unrest in almost every nation." All of this led directly to World War II. How costly was that war?

"World War II killed more persons, cost more money, damaged more property, affected more people, and probably caused more far-reaching changes than any other war in history. . . . It has been estimated that the number of war dead, civilian and military, totaled more than 22,000,000. The number of wounded has been estimated as more than 34,000,000."[226]

That is a total of over 56,000,000 casualties, almost 20,000,000 more than in World War I. Truly, the "pangs of distress" were becoming more acute as the "last days" moved toward their end!

This is also true of other catastrophes, such as food shortages. During and after World War I there was much starvation. The same was true during and after World War II. In fact, the same source noted above says that "more died of starvation" than in World War I, and adds:

"The war left millions in Europe and Asia without adequate food, shelter, or clothing. They lacked fuel, machinery, raw materials, and money. Their farms lay devastated. Infant mortality and disease were high."[227]

Of food shortages, a report in *Look* magazine in 1946 observed:

"A fourth of the world is starving today. Tomorrow will even be worse. Famine over most of the world now is more terrible than most of us can imagine. . . . There are now more people hunting desperately for food than at any other time in history."[228]

And, because of the population explosion that has taken place since World War II, the situation has not improved, but has become aggravated. Of India, *U.S. News & World Report* says:

"A natural calamity almost unprecedented in modern times is facing this nation. . . . Widespread famine, of a kind not seen in the world in this generation, is expected as the inevitable consequence unless outside aid can come."[229]

VIOLENCE, IMMORALITY, DEGENERACY

Jesus also said that there would be an "increasing of lawlessness." (Matthew 24:12) The apostle Paul foretold juvenile delinquency, violence, corruption and selfishness gone to seed: "In the last days . . . men will be lovers of themselves, . . . disobedient to parents, . . . without self-control, fierce, without love of goodness, . . . lovers of pleasures rather than lovers of God, . . . wicked men and impostors will advance from bad to worse."—2 Timothy 3:1-5, 13.

The record of our time, verified in the daily news headlines, shouts out that these things are happening right now! Note this report:

> "Fighting that sometimes resembled guerrilla warfare raged in the streets of American cities . . . A wave of crime and rioting is sweeping across the United States . . . In many cities, women are afraid to go out after dark. And they have good reason. Rapes, assaults, sadistic outbursts of senseless violence are on the rise. Crimes often seem to be committed out of sheer savagery . . . Respect for law and order is declining."[230]

This is not confined to one country. Reports from all over the world are similar. From the Philippines: "No Filipino is safe in the streets today. . . . thrill killing, vandalism, and general mayhem is steadily increasing."[231] South Korea: "We can't have even one day of peaceful life in Seoul because in the evenings the streets become streets of terror."[232] Sweden: "These critical situations that are a worry to all are expected to become even more severe."[233] England: "General lawlessness is greater—a breakdown of the sense of duty and of obligation and truthfulness."[234] And the Communist countries? "Almost everywhere, including Soviet Russia, there appears to be an increase in crime, and particularly, alas, in juvenile crime."[235]

What is happening all over the world is just as the head of the Federal Bureau of Investigation in the United States said of his land: "Citizens of this country ought to be able to walk all the streets of our cities without being mugged, raped, or robbed. But we can't do that today. All through the country, almost without exception, this condition prevails."[236]

And immorality is sweeping the world like a forest fire. In the United States the number of children born out of wedlock has more than doubled since 1945. In Latin America the rates are many times higher. "For every 1,000 live births, 716 are illegitimate in Guatemala, 613 in El Salvador, 739 in Panama and 240 in Argentina."[237] "Uruguay produced a figure of three abortions for every live birth."[238]

In Great Britain editor and author Malcolm Muggeridge said: "The position of this country . . . in my opinion, is absolutely ghastly." When asked about the rebellion of British youth against the old values, he replied: "I think it's sheer degeneracy. . . . They're just degenerate . . . the antics of an exhausted stock."[239] Another source reported: "The collapse of private morality in Britain is becoming the talk of a wondering world."[240]

ANGUISH OF NATIONS

A dean of American education told a meeting of teachers that the human race today is "just about lost." He added: "All the things that happened since 1914 are things that 'just couldn't happen' and we will see a lot more of them."[241]

Hence, what has happened since the "last days"

began in 1914 is just as Jesus foretold: "On the earth anguish of nations, not knowing the way out . . . men become faint out of fear and expectation of the things coming upon the inhabited earth." (Luke 21:25, 26) Of this very fear, columnist David Lawrence stated: "The fact is that today the biggest single emotion which dominates our lives is fear."[242]

It is little wonder, for aside from skyrocketing violence, crime, hunger, disease and immorality, mankind has another dread. The New York *Times* reported the United States Secretary of Defense as saying that "more than 120 million Americans would die in the event of a Soviet missile attack . . . If it were to include urban centers, . . . the death toll would be 149 million."[243]

There is no escaping it. All the lines of the "fingerprint" are there to see. They show conclusively that we have been in the "last days" since 1914.

EVOLUTION TEACHING MUST SHARE BLAME

Evolution teaching must take its share of the blame for the progressive worsening of crime, delinquency, immorality and even war. In this regard the well-known historian H. G. Wells made some interesting observations. In his book *The Outline of History* he noted how, in the latter half of the nineteenth century, intellectuals seized upon Darwin's explanation of evolution. They used it as a weapon against the tyranny and authority of the church. Soon the evolution theory gained widespread acceptance. But with what result? Wells, an evolutionist himself, admitted:

> "The Darwinian movement took formal Christianity unawares, suddenly. . . . The immediate effect of this great dispute . . . was very detrimental indeed. The new biological science was

bringing nothing constructive as yet to replace the old moral stand-bys. A real de-moralization ensued . . . There was a real loss of faith after 1859. The true gold of religion was in many cases thrown away with the worn-out purse that had contained it for so long, and it was not recovered. . . . Prevalent peoples at the close of the nineteenth century believed that they prevailed by virtue of the Struggle for Existence, in which the strong and cunning get the better of the weak and confiding. . . .

"Man, they decided, is a social animal like the Indian hunting dog. . . . so it seemed right to them that the big dogs of the human pack should bully and subdue."[244]

This demoralization reached national proportions. Particularly was this true of the German nation. Wells notes: "The German people was methodically indoctrinated with the idea of a German world-predominance based on might, and with the theory that war was a necessary thing in life." The anti-Christian German philosopher, Nietzsche, said: "It is mere illusion and pretty sentiment to expect much (even anything at all) from mankind if it forgets how to make war."[245] And by whom was Nietzsche influenced? Professor Will Durant said: "Nietzsche was the child of Darwin."[246]

Following the general acceptance of the evolution theory, a far more reckless age of violence developed, to which history clearly testifies. We have had two horrible world wars and now we have the threat of a third one. Morals have broken down and, for multitudes, faith in God has been shattered. The prominent evolutionist Sir Arthur Keith once confessed: "By the absorption of this new knowledge, my youthful creed was smashed to atoms. My personal God, Creator of Heaven and Earth, melted away. The desire to pray—

not the need—was lost; for one cannot pray for help to an abstraction."[247]

Evolution has thus paved the way for an increase in agnosticism and atheism as well as opening the door for communism! What the godless and Communist elements of society thought of the teaching of evolution can be noted in De Beer's book, *Charles Darwin,* which says:

> "It was no doubt partly Darwin's lack of any sense of history that led him to write his astonishingly naïve letter to Baron von Scherzer: 'What a foolish idea seems to prevail in Germany on the connection between Socialism and Evolution through Natural Selection.' That was on December 26, 1879, and a year later he must have had a shock when he received a letter from Karl Marx asking him permission to dedicate the English edition of *Das Kapital* to him."[248]

Yes, Karl Marx, the "father" of modern communism, was so delighted with Darwin's evolution work that he wanted to dedicate a book to him! He felt that Darwin's theory gave a basis in natural science for the class struggle he taught. In fact, the teaching of evolution in Western lands, in Christendom, often paves the way for persons to accept communism and other godless ideologies.

So both Nietzsche and Marx were profoundly influenced by Darwin's evolution ideas. They applied to the social and political realm what Darwin attempted to apply to the biological realm. The fruits of such thinking are seen in communism, anarchism, facism and nazism. There is no question about it. The teaching of evolution has paved the way for many 'isms' that have worked to the hurt of the human family.

It is true that an attempt has been made by some persons to harmonize belief in God with belief in evolution by saying that God created life as a one-celled organism and then guided its evolution to man. There are clergymen who accept this view. However, these clergymen, whether they realize it or not, contribute to the general moral breakdown. In order to accept the evolutionists' views, they have had to reject the Bible's account of how God created man directly. By holding that this part of the Bible is not true, they undermine confidence in the rest of the Bible, including its principles of high morality. So they reap what they sow. By preaching evolution they sow distrust in the Bible, and they reap disrespect for its good standards of morality.

Under the influence of the teaching of evolution there are clergymen who now are saying that "God is dead." They are parroting a phrase Nietzsche used. They help to plant the seed of moral decay sown by evolution, which is contributing to the inhumanity man has been showing to man and to his beastly lack of compassion. This has contributed to the abandoning of God by many clergymen and laymen, the very thing that Satan has had as his objective.

NOT MUCH LONGER

The end of all the chaotic conditions in this system of things will not be delayed. But when will it come? After enumerating the many unpleasant conditions marking this "time of the end," Jesus added the key thought: "This generation will by no means pass away until all these things occur." (Matthew 24:34) Which generation did he mean? The one that would see the beginning of the woes he mentioned. Thus the generation living in 1914 can expect to see the end of this wicked system of things.

It is to be carefully noted that the youngest of those who saw with understanding the developing sign of the "last days" from their start in 1914 are now well over sixty years of age. The greater part of the adult generation of that time is now well along toward its complete passing away.

The time left, then, is definitely limited. It is very short. Note, too, that Jesus pointedly said: "This generation *will by no means pass away* until all these things occur." The end of this wicked system and of all wickedness will come before all members of that generation pass away.

So in answer to the question: 'How much longer will it be?' the Bible replies, 'Not long, for the end of wickedness is near.' Not much longer will the Creator, Jehovah God, tolerate the wicked system of things that has continually reproached his name and often blamed him for its failures, and for the suffering it has caused. Not much longer will he permit false religious teachers and godless scientists and politicians to deceive the people. Not much longer will he permit false ideologies to turn people away from him and his Word of truth. Not much longer will he permit Satan to be the invisible ruler of the world. For a certainty cataclysmic times are fast approaching. A climax in man's history is at the door.

WHAT THE END MEANS

The end of this system of things does not mean the end of humanity. What will end will be wicked people and wicked governments. Psalm 37:9, 10 gives us this information: "Evildoers themselves will be cut off, . . . just a little while longer, and the wicked one will be no more." Showing that there will be survivors, verse 34 says: "Hope in Jehovah and keep his way, and he will exalt you to take possession of the earth. When the wicked ones are cut off, you will see it." Persons who look to God as their guide will see the end of this wicked system of things. They will survive it and begin repopulating the earth.

While rulership of mankind will not end, the wicked rule under which mankind groans today will. God's inspired Word assures us of righteous rule by God's kingdom:

"In the days of those kings the God of heaven will set up a kingdom that will never be brought to ruin. And the kingdom itself will not be passed on to any other people. It will crush and put an end to all these kingdoms [existing today], and it itself will stand to times indefinite."—Daniel 2:44.

Rulership will be taken away from mankind and from Satan the Devil. God will rule this earth by means of the kingdom that people have prayed for when they repeated the "Lord's prayer," or the "Our Father" prayer. That kingdom is a literal government, a just working arrangement that is specifically designed to control human affairs on earth. God places it in the hands of an obedient spirit creature who has proved worthy of the position of King of that kingdom. That spirit creature is Jesus Christ, now in heavenly glory.

No longer will man rule man. But God, through this heavenly government, will rule mankind in righteousness. That government will be incorruptible and beyond the reach of any creature or rebellious group to overthrow. It will rule in justice, righteousness and peace for the good of mankind forever.—Isaiah 9:6, 7.

At the time that God displays his tremendous power and puts an end to injustice, crime, violence, false religion and imperfect human governments there will be no doubt that the God of Creation exists. Then will be fulfilled what is written at Psalm 83:18: "That people may know that you, whose name is Jehovah, you alone are the Most High over all the earth."

HEAVENLY GOVERNMENT ALREADY AT WORK

All the evidence in fulfillment of Bible prophecy proves that we are in the "last days," nearing the end of this wicked system. But, of necessity, it means something more. It means that the heavenly government, the kingdom for which Jesus taught Christians to pray, is already in operation! (Matthew 6:9, 10) Why so? Because the beginning of the "last days" in 1914 coincided with the invisible presence of Jesus Christ in Kingdom power. Yes, that heavenly government is already in action. Its first act was to cast Satan and his demons out of heaven down to the immediate vicinity of the earth, thus cleansing the heavenly realm of wicked creatures.—Psalm 110:1, 2; Revelation 12:7-12.

Since that time God has caused to be carried out a worldwide preaching work in fulfillment of the prophecy at Matthew 24:14, where Jesus stated: "This good news of the kingdom will be preached in all the inhabited earth for a witness to all the nations; and then the end will come." As a result of this preaching activity, many hundreds of thousands of people from all nations are being liberated from bondage to false religion. Because they cease making themselves a part of the Devil's political system they enjoy unity and peace.

These people acknowledge themselves to be subjects of the heavenly kingdom and are demonstrating the effectiveness of that government. Under its direction they have learned to become

law-abiding, moral and upright, persons of integrity. They no longer war against one another.
. . . Rioting, hatred, crime, divisive nationalism, hypocrisy, dishonesty and immorality that disrupt this world are not practiced within their ranks.

These people line themselves up with God's righteous requirements, requirements that have worked to their good. They are living testimony to the fact that God's ways work for good, but that man's ways that are outside of God's ways, and the ways of Satan, work for man's detriment. The two systems stand in stark contrast. The failure of human wisdom alone to bring the peace and unity now enjoyed in nearly two hundred lands by Jehovah's witnesses is evident in the United Nations. It has not been able to bring peace and unity among its members, much less for the entire world. Why is this so? Because the United Nations is based on man's wisdom alone, and Jeremiah 10:23 warned: "To earthling man his way does not belong. It does not belong to man who is walking even to direct his step." And Psalm 127:1 adds: "Unless Jehovah himself builds the house, it is to no avail that its builders have worked hard on it."

But when persons throughout the world submit to God's guidance and acknowledge the rulership of his heavenly government, the results are in startling contrast to this crumbling wicked system. By not rebelling against the rulership of God, but by submitting to it, God-fearing ones are able to come in line with what Isaiah 2:4 foretold: "[God] will certainly render judgment among the nations and set matters straight respecting many peoples. And they will have to beat their swords into plowshares and their spears into pruning shears. Nation will not lift up sword against nation, neither will they learn war any more."

That condition exists today among worshipers of the Creator, Jehovah God. They have listened to what God has to say, as Isaiah also noted: "[God] will instruct us about his ways, and we will walk in his paths." (Isaiah 2:3) It is obedience to instruction that comes from Jehovah God that enables people from all walks of life, in all nations, to demonstrate that his government is the only hope for mankind's survival. It is the only right way, and it is working marvelously now!

But what God has done in this regard now is only the beginning. Much more is due to come shortly.

CHAPTER 15

A Marvelous Future

HOW different will be the new era, when God brings an end to wickedness! Instead of sorrow, sickness and death, there will be happiness, vibrant health and everlasting life! The nightmare of the past will be gone forever. The joy at that time will far outweigh all the agony man has ever experienced. All this God will do for man by transforming the earth into a paradise. As Psalm 145:16 says: "You [God] are opening your hand and satisfying the desire of every living thing."

Nothing can stand in the way of the fulfillment of God's purposes. What he has promised he will do without fail: "So my word that goes forth from my mouth will prove to be. It will not return to me without results, but it will certainly do that in which I have delighted, and it will have certain success in that for which I have sent it." —Isaiah 55:11.

THE WICKED REMOVED

God's destruction of the wicked at the end of this system of things will bring an end to murder, rape, robbery and every other kind of crime. Think of it, no more wickedness! No longer will righteously disposed persons have to suffer at the hands of wicked people. Proverbs 10:30 promises: "As for the righteous one, to time indefinite he will not be caused to stagger; but as for the wicked ones, they will not keep residing on the earth."

With wicked humans and wicked demons gone, righteousness will prevail earth wide. Under the benevolent administration of God's kingdom, earth's inhabitants will not learn what is bad. No more will they learn things that work to the hurt of humankind. Instead, "righteousness is what the inhabitants of the productive land will certainly learn." No one will be misled by false religion or pseudoscientific theories such as evolution. Because everyone will be taught the truth, the following prophecy will be fulfilled: "The earth will certainly be filled with the knowledge of Jehovah as the waters are covering the very sea."—Isaiah 26:9; 11:9; Acts 17:31.

Not only will wickedness cease and ignorance be removed, but there will also be a rolling back of all the ill effects of the original rebellion by the first human pair.

HEALTH RESTORED

God will greatly bless mankind by eliminating the great unhappiness and suffering caused by poor health. Cancer, heart trouble and other diseases take the lives of multitudes now. Thousands, yes, millions of others suffer by being crippled, blind or deaf. Even if you enjoy a measure of good health, the distressing reality in this system of things is that as you grow old, your eyes dim, your teeth decay, your hearing dulls, your skin wrinkles, your internal organs break down, until finally death claims another victim.

However, these distressing things that we inherited from our first parents will be a thing of the past in God's new order. Since God created man, he is also able to heal him permanently of those diseases that daily take the lives of multitudes. He is able to make the crippled walk, the blind see and the deaf hear. He has promised to do all this. We have an assurance of it because the King of God's kingdom did it on a small scale 1,900 years ago.

Miraculous acts of healing by Jesus Christ demonstrated what shall be done earth wide in the new era. Of one instance, the Bible says: "Great crowds approached him, having along with them people that were lame, maimed, blind, dumb, and many otherwise, and they fairly threw them at his feet, *and he cured them;* so that the crowd felt amazement as they saw the dumb speaking and the lame walking and the blind seeing." —Matthew 15:30, 31.

Imagine the happiness that will come in God's new order as all human ills are eliminated, not just in one small area, but earth wide! The Creator's promise is: "No resident will say: 'I am sick.'" As to his healing power he says: "The eyes of the blind ones will be opened, and the very ears of the deaf ones will be unstopped. At that time the lame one will climb up just as a stag does, and the tongue of the speechless one will cry out in gladness."—Isaiah 33:24; 35:5, 6.

Will it not be thrilling to wake up each morning to a new day and realize that you are healthier than you were the day before, instead of being one day closer to the grave? And will it not be gratifying for elderly persons to know that they will become more youthful as each twenty-four-hour period passes, until they gradually reach the perfection of body and mind that Adam and Eve originally enjoyed?

Having that kind of health and the happiness that is promised to come, no one will want to die, and no one will have to die! Why not? Because even death will be done away with, since mankind will no longer be in the grip of inherited sin. Jesus Christ, as the head of God's heavenly government over man, "must rule as king until God has put all enemies under his feet. As the last enemy, death is to be brought to nothing." We also read: "He will actually swallow up death forever." God's promises concerning everlasting life will be fully realized. We are told: "The gift God gives is everlasting life by Christ Jesus our Lord."—1 Corinthians 15:25, 26; Isaiah 25:8; Romans 6:23.

Summing up the benefits that will flow to the human family in the paradisaic new era of God's making, the last book of the Bible says: "And [God] will wipe out every tear from their eyes, and death will be no more, neither will mourning nor outcry nor pain be any more. The former things have passed away."—Revelation 21:3, 4.

BRINGING BACK DEAD ONES

However, what of all those who are already dead, who are in their graves, such as persons who may have been dear to you? Will they always remain there?

Keep in mind that, while on earth, Jesus not only cured the sick and maimed, but he also brought back dead persons from the sleep of death. This demonstrated the wonderful power God has for resurrecting the dead, a power he granted to Jesus Christ. Perhaps you recall the occasion when Jesus came to the house of a man whose twelve-year-old daughter had died. Addressing himself to the dead girl, Jesus declared: "Maiden, I say to you, Get up!" What was the result? The Bible tells us: "And immediately the maiden rose and began walking." How did the people that saw this marvelous miracle react? "At once they were beside themselves with great ecstasy." They were overjoyed. Their happiness could hardly be contained.—Mark 5:41, 42.

In the paradisaic new era Jesus will use this God-given power to raise the dead. It is written about that time that "there is going to be a resurrection of both the righteous and the unrighteous." (Acts 24:15) How great will be the joy earth wide when group after group of dead persons will come back to life! Imagine the happy reunions there will be of loved relatives! Instead of obituary columns that bring sadness, there may well be announcements of newly resurrected ones to bring joy to those who loved them.

All those coming back in the resurrection will be educated in what is right. They will not be hindered by false religious doctrines and pseudo-scientific theories that have worked to man's hurt. They will all receive the truth about human history, God's purposes and his requirements for mankind. No one will have to wonder where he came from and where he is going. Everyone will know. By the fact that they will have been brought back from the dead, re-created to life, they will be compelled to acknowledge that man is the product of divine creation, not evolution. What a test that will be of the humility of resurrected persons who had believed and taught the evolution theory!

PERFECT PEACE

Peace in all areas of life will be realized. Wars will be a thing of the past, for divisive national interests will disappear. "They will not lift up sword, nation against nation, neither will they learn war any more." (Micah 4:3) This may sound astonishing in view of growing international difficulties in our day, but note the Bible's promise: "Come, you people, behold the activities of Jehovah, how he has set astonishing events

on the earth. He is making wars to cease to the extremity of the earth. The bow he breaks apart and does cut the spear in pieces; the wagons he burns in the fire."—Psalm 46:8, 9.

Peace will also be restored between man and beast. In this regard the Creator declares: "For them I shall certainly conclude a covenant in that day in connection with the wild beast of the field and with the flying creature of the heavens and the creeping thing of the ground and . . . I will make them lie down in security." —Hosea 2:18.

Just how great the restored peace between man and beast that had existed in the garden of Eden will be can be noted in this prophecy:

> "The wolf will actually reside for a while with the male lamb, and with the kid the leopard itself will lie down, and the calf and the maned young lion and the well-fed animal all together; *and a mere little boy will be leader over them.* And the cow and the bear themselves will feed; together their young ones will lie down. And even the lion will eat straw just like the bull. And the sucking child will certainly play upon the hole of the cobra; and upon the light aperture of a poisonous snake will a weaned child actually put his own hand. They will not do any harm or cause any ruin in all my holy mountain."—Isaiah 11:6-9.

Why no harm among men and beasts? Why perfect peace? Because, as previously noted, "the earth will certainly be filled with the knowledge

of Jehovah as the waters are covering the very sea." God's ways are the ways that bring peace. What a contrast to the ways of rebellious men and demons who chose the course of independence from God!

EARTH TRANSFORMED

What of the earth itself? It will be transformed into a luxuriant paradise. That is why Jesus could promise the evildoer that was executed with him: "You will be with me in Paradise."—Luke 23:43.

Under the direction of God's kingdom, the earth will produce abundantly good things for man to eat. Hunger will never again stalk the earth. "There will come to be plenty of grain on the earth; on the top of the mountains there will be an overflow." "The earth itself will certainly give its produce; God, our God, will bless us." "The tree of the field must give its fruitage, and the land itself will give its yield, and they will actually prove to be on their soil in security." —Psalms 72:16; 67:6; Ezekiel 34:27.

Everyone then will have his own property to cultivate and to enjoy. He will be in no danger of greedy men getting possession of what he has. The good things of the earth will be for all to enjoy. The Creator illustrates this by saying:

"They will certainly build houses and have occupancy; and they will certainly plant vineyards and eat their fruitage. They will not build and someone else have occupancy; they will not plant and someone else do the eating. For like the days of a tree will the days of my people be; and the work of their own hands my chosen ones will use to the full. They will not toil for nothing, nor will they bring to birth for disturbance." —Isaiah 65:21-23.

"Just a little while longer, and the wicked one will be no more; . . . But the meek ones themselves will possess the earth, and they will indeed find their exquisite delight in the abundance of peace. . . . The righteous themselves will possess the earth, and they will reside forever upon it."—Psalm 37:10, 11, 29

The prophecy at Micah 4:4 suggests the sense of security that will be had then by saying: "They will actually sit, each one under his vine and under his fig tree, and there will be no one making them tremble." This will mean that there will never again be people living in fear because their neighborhood is overrun with crime or is shaken by riots. The rule of God's kingdom will ensure personal security. It will also ensure that conditions that breed dissension, such as slums and overcrowded dwellings, will be gone forever.

With bad conditions and violently wicked men no longer existing, the whole earth will become the possession of people who love righteousness. The Bible states: "The meek ones themselves will possess the earth, and they will indeed find their exquisite delight in the abundance of peace. The righteous themselves will possess the earth, and they will reside forever upon it."—Psalm 37: 11, 29.

That is how God will more than compensate for the wickedness that innocent people have suffered during their lifetime. Throughout eternity God will shower down blessings on mankind, so that any hurt they have received in the past will fade to a dim memory, if they care to remember it at all. The Creator guarantees:

> "I am creating new heavens [a new heavenly government] and a new earth [righteous human society]; and the former things will not be called to mind, neither will they come up into the heart. But exult, you people, and be joyful forever in what I am creating."—Isaiah 65:17, 18.

Persons who desire to live in that righteous new system need to take in accurate knowledge of the Creator. They should not be diverted and deceived by unscientific speculations about the origin and destiny of man. They should face the fact squarely that man got here, not by evolution, but by creation. They should also face the fact that their future will be decided, not by evolution, but by the God of creation. Then, basing their decisions on the Creator's unerring Word as a guide, they can confidently look forward to a marvelous future, trusting him to fulfill his promises.

Armed with accurate knowledge of both the Creator's Word and the facts of science, such persons will appreciate the truth of Isaiah 29:16, which says: "The perversity of you men! Should the potter himself be accounted just like the clay? For should the thing made say respecting its maker: 'He did not make me'? And does the very thing formed actually say respecting its former: 'He showed no understanding'?"

No, they will not fall into such unscientific reasoning, but will face up to the facts and confidently say, as did the ancient psalmist: "Know that Jehovah is God. It is he that has made us, and not we ourselves."—Psalm 100:3.

REFERENCES

1 The Houston *Post*, August 23, 1964, p. P-6.
2 *The River of Life*, by Rutherford Platt, 1956, p. vii.
3 *The World Book Encyclopedia*, 1966, Vol. 6, p. 330.
4 *Genetics and the Origin of Species*, by Theodosius Dobzhansky, 1951, pp. 3, 11.
5 The New York *Times*, November 29, 1959.
6 *Ibid.*, November 26, 1959.
7 *Biology for You*, by B. B. Vance and D. F. Miller, 1963, p. 531.
8 The New Orleans *Times-Picayune*, May 7, 1964.
9 The Milwaukee *Journal*, March 5, 1966, p. 5.
10 The New York *Times*, November 14, 1966, p. 40.
11 *Webster's Third New International Dictionary*, 1961, p. 813.
12 *The Origin of Species*, by Charles Darwin, *The Harvard Classics*, 1909, Vol. 11, p. 178.
13 *Science Year*, 1966, p. 197.
14 *The Biological Basis of Human Freedom*, by Theodosius Dobzhansky, 1956, pp. 6, 8, 9.
15 *Encyclopædia Britannica*, 1946, Vol. 8, pp. 916, 927; Vol. 14, p. 767.
16 *Charles Darwin*, by Sir Gavin de Beer, 1965, p. 215.

17 *The Fossil Evidence for Human Evolution*, by W. E. Le Gros Clark, 1964, pp. 41, 188.

18 *Science*, January 22, 1965, p. 389.

19 *The World Book Encyclopedia*, 1966, Vol. 6, p. 334.

20 *Science News Letter*, May 29, 1965, p. 346.

21 *The Fossil Evidence for Human Evolution*, p. 174.

22 *Science*, December 30, 1960, p. 1914.

23 *The Bible and Modern Science*, by L. Merson Davies, 1953, p. 7.

24 The Fresno *Bee*, August 20, 1959, p. 1-B.

25 *Lutheran Witness Reporter*, November 14, 1965.

26 *Charles Darwin*, p. 163.

27 *Review Text in Biology*, by Mark A. Hall and Milton S. Lesser, 1966, pp. 304, 305.

28 *Encyclopedia Britannica*, 1959, article by H. J. Muller, Vol. 22, p. 988.

29 *The Mechanism of Evolution*, by W. H. Dowdeswell, 1960, p. 14.

30 *Time*, February 12, 1965, p. 51.

31 *Biology for Today*, by Sayles B. Clark and J. Albert Mould, 1964, p. 321.

32 *The Story of Life*, by H. E. L. Mellersh, 1958, pp. 237, 242.

33 *Charles Darwin*, p. 182.

34 *Review Text in Biology*, p. 363.

35 *American Scientist*, January 1953, p. 100.

36 Oklahoma City *Times*, August 10, 1966, p. 25.

37 *The Orion Book of Evolution*, by Jean Rostand, 1961, pp. 75, 76.

38 *Science Digest*, January 1961, pp. 61-63.

39 *The Orion Book of Evolution*, p. 79.

40 *Ibid.*, p. 91.

41 *The Saturday Evening Post*, December 3, 1966, p. 42.

42 *Discovery*, May 1962, p. 44.

43 *Look*, January 16, 1962, p. 46.

44 *The Immense Journey*, by Loren Eiseley, 1957, p. 206.

45 *Science Today*, 1961, chapter by Sir James Gray, p. 21.

46 *The Ideas of Biology*, by John Tyler Bonner, 1962, p. 18.

47 The New York *Times*, November 13, 1966, p. 6E.

48 *Webster's Third New International Dictionary*, p. 7a.

49 *Reader's Digest*, January 1963, p. 92.

50 *The Immense Journey*, p. 199.

51 *Ibid.*, pp. 199, 200.

52 *The River of Life*, p. 100.

53 *Review Text in Biology*, pp. 252, 253.

54 *The Encyclopedia Americana*, 1956, Vol. 3, p. 721.

55 *Biology for You*, p. 468.

56 *Organic Evolution and the Bible*, by E. J. Gardner, 1960, pp. 11, 12.

57 *Science Year*, 1965, p. 18.

58 *The Origin of Species*, p. 190.

59 *Animal Evolution*, by G. S. Carter, 1954, p. 350.

60 *Scientific American*, May 1963, p. 53.

61 *The Minnesota Technolog*, October 1957.

62 *The Evidence of God in an Expanding Universe*, edited by John Clover Monsma, 1958, chapter by E. C. Kornfeld, p. 176.

63 *The Origin of Species*, pp. 359-361.

64 The New York *Times*, October 25, 1964, p. 8E.

65 *The World We Live In*, by the editorial staff of *Life* and Lincoln Barnett, 1955, p. 93.

66 *Scientific American*, August 1964, pp. 34-36.

67 *Natural History*, October 1959, pp. 466, 467.

68 *Ibid.*, p. 457.

69 *The Origin of Species*, pp. 178, 179, 503.

70 *Ibid.*, p. 179.

71 *Ibid.*, p. 346.

72 *The Major Features of Evolution*, by George Gaylord Simpson, 1953, p. 360.

73 *Genetics, Paleontology and Evolution*, edited by Glenn L. Jepsen, Ernst Mayr, George Gaylord Simpson, 1963, chapter by A. S. Romer, p. 114.

74 *On Growth and Form*, by D'Arcy Thompson, 1943, pp. 1092-1094.

75 *Synthetic Speciation*, by Heribert Nilsson, 1954, pp. 488, 489, translated from the German by W. E. Filmer in *Dr. Heribert Nilsson's Views on the Theory of Evolution*.

76 *Genetics and the Origin of Species*, p. 4.

77 *The Primates*, by Sarel Eimerl and Irven DeVore and the editors of *Life*, 1965, p. 15.

78 *Science News Letter*, August 25, 1951, p. 118.

79 *Human Destiny*, by Lecomte du Noüy, 1947, p. 95.

80 *Science*, December 9, 1955, p. 1144.

81 *Scientific American*, December 1966, p. 32.

82 *Genetics and the Origin of Species*, pp. 5, 6.

83 *The Material Basis of Evolution*, by Richard B. Goldschmidt, 1940, pp. 165, 168.

84 *Biology for Today*, p. 294.

85 *Genetics and the Origin of Species*, p. 96.

86 *Charles Darwin*, plate 8.

87 *The Biological Basis of Human Freedom*, p. 56.

88 *The New You and Heredity*, by Amram Scheinfeld, 1950, p. 476.

89 *Biology for Today*, p. 273.

90 *Radiation, Genes and Man*, by Bruce Wallace and Theodosius Dobzhansky, 1959, p. 35.

91 *Science Today*, chapter by C. H. Waddington, p. 36.

92 *The World Book Encyclopedia*, 1966, Vol. 13, p. 809; Vol. 9, p. 194.

93 *Time*, November 11, 1946, p. 96.

94 *The Mechanism of Evolution*, p. 30.

95 *Genetics and the Origin of Species*, p. 73.

96 *The Creationist*, December 1964, p. 90.

97 The New Zealand *Herald*, January 17, 1963, p. 16.

98 *Scientific American*, November 1955, p. 58.

99 *Progress and Decline*, by Hugh Miller, 1963, p. 38.

100 *The Bible and Modern Science*, by Henry M. Morris, 1956, p. 41.

101 *Encyclopædia Britannica*, 1946, Vol. 8, p. 922.

102 *Charles Darwin*, p. 191.

103 *Science Today*, chapter by Sir James Gray, pp. 29, 30.

104 *Ibid.*, p. 38.

105 *The Orion Book of Evolution*, p. 79.

106 *The Geography of Evolution*, by George Gaylord Simpson, 1965, p. 17.

107 *Reader's Digest*, October 1962, pp. 144, 148.

108 *Scientific American*, October 1963, p. 51.

109 *Science Year*, 1966, p. 314.

110 *Reader's Digest*, October 1962, p. 144.

111 *The Biological Basis of Human Freedom*, p. 102.

112 *Scientific American*, December 1953, pp. 71, 72.

113 *The Story of Man*, by H. E. L. Mellersh, 1959, p. 14.

114 *Life*, June 28, 1963, p. 72.

115 The New York *Times Magazine*, October 9, 1966, pp. 142, 144-146.

116 *Science News Letter*, May 29, 1965, pp. 346, 347.

117 *The Orion Book of Evolution*, p. 92.

118 *New Scientist*, March 25, 1965, p. 798.

119 *Scientific American*, June 1956, pp. 98, 100.

120 *Evolution as a Process*, edited by Julian Huxley, 1958, pp. 300-302.

121 *New Scientist*, March 25, 1965, p. 800.

122 *The Saturday Evening Post*, December 3, 1966, p. 65.

123 *The Primates*, p. 177.

124 *Scientific American*, November 1966, p. 53.

125 The New York *Times*, April 11, 1965, p. E7.

126 *Scientific American*, July 1964, p. 62.

127 The New York *Times*, April 11, 1965, p. E7.

128 *Science News*, January 28, 1967, p. 83.

129 *The Saturday Evening Post*, December 3, 1966, pp. 48, 49.
130 *The Fossil Evidence for Human Evolution*, p. 175.
131 The New York *Times*, April 11, 1965, p. E7.
132 *The Primates*, p. 178.
133 *The Fossil Evidence for Human Evolution*, p. 172.
134 *Science*, December 13, 1957, p. 1238.
135 *Ibid.*, November 29, 1957, p. 1108.
136 *The Long Road to Man*, by Robert L. Lehrman, 1961, p. 115.
137 *Man: His First Million Years*, by Ashley Montagu, 1957, p. 51.
138 *The World Book Encyclopedia*, 1966, Vol. 15, p. 669.
139 *The Encyclopedia Americana*, 1956, Vol. 18, p. 185.
140 *Scientific American*, May 1965, p. 50.
141 *Ibid.*, November 1966, p. 53.
142 *Biology and Its Relation to Mankind*, by A. M. Winchester, 1964, p. 604.
143 *The World Book Encyclopedia*, 1966, Vol. 15, p. 672.
144 *Harper's*, December 1962, p. 73.
145 The New York *Times Magazine*, March 19, 1961, p. 30.
146 *The World Book Encyclopedia*, 1966, Vol. 15, p. 672.
147 *Ibid.*, Vol. 7, p. 25.
148 *Science Digest*, April 1951, p. 33.
149 Chicago *Tribune*, April 21, 1963.
150 *Biology and Its Relation to Mankind*, p. 604.
151 *Evolution or Special Creation?*, by Frank Lewis Marsh, 1963, p. 26.
152 *The Bible and Modern Science*, H. M. Morris, pp. 52, 53.
153 *The Fossil Evidence for Human Evolution*, p. 54.
154 *Man, God and Magic*, by Ivar Lissner, 1961, p. 304.
155 The New York *Times*, September 7, 1959.
156 *Encyclopœdia Britannica*, 1946, Vol. 14, p. 763.
157 *The Fossil Evidence for Human Evolution*, pp. 26, 27.
158 *Encyclopœdia Britannica*, 1946, Vol. 14, p. 763.
159 *Science News Letter*, February 25, 1961, p. 119.
160 *Reader's Digest*, October 1956, p. 182.
161 *Scientific American*, January 1965, p. 52.
162 *The Primates*, p. 177.
163 *Reader's Digest*, November 1966, pp. 229, 235.
164 *Encyclopœdia Britannica*, 1946, Vol. 8, p. 926.
165 *Science*, December 10, 1965, p. 1490.
166 *Science Digest*, December 1960, p. 19.
167 *Science Year*, 1966, p. 193.
168 *Science*, December 11, 1959, p. 1630.
169 *Ibid.*, August 16, 1963, p. 634.
170 The New York *Times*, January 14, 1967, p. 1.
171 *Scientific American*, September 1961, p. 86.
172 *Natural History*, February 1967, p. 58.
173 *Science*, April 2, 1965, p. 73.
174 *Ibid.*, April 27, 1962, pp. 293-295.
175 *Science Digest*, December 1962, p. 35.
176 *Newsweek*, December 23, 1963, p. 48.
177 *Science Year*, 1965, pp. 215, 217.
178 *The Saturday Evening Post*, January 16, 1960, pp. 39, 82, 83.
179 *Ibid.*, January 10, 1959, p. 66.
180 *Science*, March 3, 1961, p. 624.
181 *The World Book Encyclopedia*, 1966, Vol. 6, p. 12.
182 *The Encyclopedia Americana*, 1956, Vol. 10, p. 613b.
183 *Biology for Today*, p. 327.
184 *Review Text in Biology*, p. 354.
185 *Man: His First Million Years*, p. 116.
186 *Biology and Its Relation to Mankind*, p. 600.
187 *Man: His First Million Years*, p. 21.
188 *Biology and Human Progress*, by Louis Eisman and Charles Tanzer, 1958, p. 509.
189 *New Discoveries in Babylonia About Genesis*, by P. J. Wiseman, 1949, p. 28.
190 *Science World*, February 1, 1961, p. 5.
191 *The Encyclopedia Americana*, 1956, Vol. 10, pp. 613a, 613b.

192 The New York *Times,* January 8, 1950, pp. 1, 28.
193 *Science Year,* 1966, p. 256.
194 *Science News Letter,* September 3, 1955, p. 148.
195 *Man: His First Million Years,* p. 116.
196 *Encyclopædia Britannica,* 1966, Vol. 14, p. 738.
197 The New York *Times,* October 30, 1966, p. E7.
198 *The Orion Book of Evolution,* p. 95.
199 San Francisco *Examiner & Chronicle,* September 11, 1966, p. 30.
200 *The First Nine Months,* by Geraldine L. Flanagan, 1962, p. 25.
201 *Science Today,* pp. 25, 26.
202 *The Nature of Life,* by C. H. Waddington, 1962, p. 67.
203 *Life,* April 30, 1965, pp. 70, 72A.
204 *Ibid.,* p. 72A.
205 *Ibid.*
206 *Ibid.,* p. 54.
207 *Reader's Digest,* May 1962, p. 154.
208 *Natural History,* November 1961, p. 17.
209 *Bionics the Science of "Living" Machines,* by Daniel S. Halacy, Jr., 1965, flyleaf.
210 *Ibid.,* p. 55.
211 *Marvels and Mysteries of Our Animal World,* by The Reader's Digest Association, 1964, p. 237.
212 *The Mysterious Senses of Animals,* by V. B. Dröscher, 1965, pp. 175, 176.
213 *The Orion Book of Evolution,* p. 95.
214 *American Scientist,* January 1953, p. 105.
215 *Evolution, Creation and Science,* by Frank Lewis Marsh, 1947, p. 10.
216 *Modern Science and Christian Faith,* by members of The American Scientific Affiliation, 1950, p. 65.
217 *The Biblical Flood and the Ice Epoch,* by Donald W. Patten, 1966, p. 267.
218 *Report,* June 1966, p. 19.
219 *The Basic Teachings of the Great Philosophers,* by S. E. Frost, Jr., 1942, p. 296.
220 *Life,* March 13, 1964, p. 45.
221 *The World Book Encyclopedia,* 1966, Vol. 20, p. 377.
222 London *Evening Star,* quoted in the New Orleans *Times-Picayune,* August 5, 1960.
223 The New York *Times Magazine,* August 1, 1954, p. 9.
224 Cleveland *West Parker,* January 20, 1966, p. 1.
225 *U.S. News & World Report,* September 13, 1965, p. 20.
226 *The World Book Encyclopedia,* 1966, Vol. 20, pp. 379, 380, 410.
227 *Ibid.,* pp. 410, 411.
228 *Look,* June 11, 1946.
229 *U.S. News & World Report,* December 27, 1965, p. 58.
230 *Ibid.,* August 1, 1966, pp. 5, 46, 47.
231 Philippine Islands *Weekly Graphic,* May 13, 1964.
232 South Korea *Chosun Daily,* April 14, 1964.
233 Stockholm *Vecko-Journalen,* May 14, 1964, p. 24.
234 *Look,* September 24, 1963, p. 74.
235 *U.S. News & World Report,* November 1, 1965, pp. 67, 69.
236 *Ibid.,* September 19, 1966, p. 43.
237 *Science News Letter,* May 18, 1963, p. 309.
238 *Look,* July 14, 1964.
239 *U.S. News & World Report,* July 25, 1966, pp. 67, 69.
240 *Intelligence Digest,* September 1966, p. 4.
241 St. Paul *Dispatch,* January 19, 1963, p. 2.
242 *U.S. News & World Report,* October 11, 1965, p. 144.
243 The New York *Times,* February 19, 1965, p. 1.
244 *The Outline of History,* by H. G. Wells, 1921, pp. 956, 957.
245 *Ibid.,* p. 1005.
246 *The Story of Philosophy,* by Will Durant, 1943, p. 301.
247 *The Forum,* April 1930, p. 223.
248 *Charles Darwin,* p. 266.

HAVE YOU ASKED THESE QUESTIONS?

● **Why believe in God when man cannot see him?**

● **What happens to us when we die? Will the dead ever live again?**

● **What proves that the Bible is the only book inspired by God?**

These and other vital questions that affect your future are discussed in the internationally distributed book "Things in Which It Is Impossible for God to Lie." Millions of copies have been obtained by people in nearly 200 lands. Its 416 pages are filled with information that satisfies the truth-seeking mind. The cost is only 50 cents.

Send for your copy to any of these addresses: